The MACHINERY *of* LIFE

DEAN E. WOOLDRIDGE

Research Associate
California Institute of Technology

The MACHINERY
of LIFE

McGRAW-HILL BOOK COMPANY

New York San Francisco Toronto London Sydney

THE MACHINERY OF LIFE

1234567890VB721069876

Acknowledgments

In preparing this book I have received extensive assistance from two of my friends and associates: James Bonner of the California Institute of Technology, and Duane Roller of Harvey Mudd College. Because of his extensive familiarity with current biological research, Dr. Bonner was able to make many suggestions that improved the scientific accuracy and adequacy of the manuscript. Dr. Roller's extensive editorial efforts contributed greatly to whatever clarity was ultimately achieved in the exposition.

In addition, a number of the experts whose work I referenced were kind enough to read parts of the material and provide corrections and suggestions for changes. Without implying that these men necessarily endorse the book, but only for the purpose of gratefully acknowledging their assistance, I list their names here: G. W. Beadle, University of Chicago; Melvin Calvin, University of California at Berkeley; F. Crick, Cambridge University; J. B. Gurdon, Oxford University; F. Jacob, Pasteur Institute, Paris; Maclyn McCarty, Rockefeller Institute; F. Sanger, Cambridge University; W. M. Stanley, University of California at Berkeley; E. L. Tatum, Rockefeller Institute; and M. H. F. Wilkins, King's College, London.

Dean E. Wooldridge

Contents

The MACHINERY *of* LIFE

Introduction

One of our innate characteristics, as human animals, appears to be a need to "understand" what goes on around us. Because of the way our minds are constructed, we cannot avoid seeking "causes" for the "effects" that we observe through our sensory mechanisms. Since physiological limitations prevent our holding in mind and dealing simultaneously with more than a few related concepts, we continually strive to reduce to a minimum the number of fundamental causes or principles that we employ to explain what we observe. There is more than a little of the scientist built into the genetic specifications of each human individual.

The fact that the universe in which we live is largely susceptible to understanding in terms of the kind of cause/effect principles that man naturally searches for no longer seems to be the mysterious coincidence that it once appeared. We now appreciate how the operation of evolution and natural selection must automatically, in time, bring to dominance animal species with behavior and thought patterns that adapt them well to their envi-

1

ronment. If the universe operates largely on the basis of cause/ effect relationships, we would expect that the dominant species would owe its dominance largely to its evolutionarily developed ability to deal competently with cause/effect situations.

A paradoxical consequence of man's natural predilection for logical thought was his invention of the important concept of the supernatural. He had a compulsion to explain what he observed, but his ability to trace cause/effect relationships was limited to the simpler, more immediate phenomena of his environment. To provide an "explanation" for matters he despaired of understanding, he invented the concept that these matters lay outside the domain of natural cause/effect principles—that, in short, they were "supernatural." This was appealing to the orderly human mind: it provided a neat means of differentiating between the aspects of life that ought to be dealt with rationally and those which should be just accepted but not analyzed.

The development of science can be described as the process of transferring one after another aspect of human experience from the supernatural category into the realm of natural law. The rain and wind, lightning and earthquake, the rising and setting of the sun and stars have long since been accepted as the manifestations of the workings of the laws of gravity, mechanics, thermodynamics, and electricity. In more modern times the aurora borealis, the Van Allen belt, the propagation of radio waves, the properties of chemical dyes and plastics, and the principles of rocket propulsion are all "understood" in terms of generally accepted natural laws. And there are surprisingly few of these laws. With a couple of dozen subnuclear particles and a similar number of fundamental physical laws we are today able to derive explanations for a tremendous variety of physical and chemical phenomena, and most of those we cannot explain appear to be beyond our reach because of their complexity, rather than because of any inadequacy in the fundamental laws. To be sure, the last word has not yet been said relative to the basic particles from which matter and energy are derived and we have good reason to believe that we have not yet precisely formulated the natural laws, since new discoveries require us to refine and restate them from time to time. We cannot even be sure that there do not still exist undiscovered phenomena whose explanation will require major additions to our present statement of the body of natural law. However, all this is beside the point. The fact that our knowledge of the laws and particles that govern and inhabit the universe is less than perfect must not obscure the tremendous body of evidence attesting to the orderliness of all natural phenomena that are generally classified as "physical" or "chemical." In this very broad area the crutch of a supernatural explanation now has to be used almost not at all.

Almost, but not quite. The explanations of physical phenomena must always start with the fundamental particles and the natural laws. Assuming the laws always existed and the particles were somehow provided in suitable number and distribution, plausible theories can be devised for the formation of the stars, the plants, the galaxies, and even for the subsequent course of billions of years of geologic development that have made of the earth what it is today. But since science is by its very nature based upon the process of reasoning from cause to effect, or of deducing probable causes from known effects, it is intrinsically incapable of carrying us back behind first causes. No scientist can "explain" the natural laws on which his science is ultimately based. He may invent a term such as "gravitational attraction" to enable him to discuss a phenomenon he wishes to deal with, and he may agree with other scientists on techniques for measuring the gravitational attraction between material objects. He may then perform experiments that ultimately permit him to deduce relations, or "laws," connecting gravitational forces and the masses and positions of the bodies involved. Thus he can learn how to predict the gravitational effects that will be produced by a specified configuration of objects or, conversely, to arrive at valid configurational deductions in terms of measured gravitational forces. But what *is* gravity, really? What causes it? Where does it come from? How did it get started? The scientist has no answers. His delineation of the relations between gravitational forces and other properties of matter and space, and his discovery that the relationships so delineated are immutable and unchanging, may cause him to develop such a sense of familiarity with gravity that he is no longer curious about it. Nevertheless, in a fundamental sense, it is still as mysterious and inexplicable as it ever was, and it seems destined to remain so. Science can never tell us why the natural laws of physics exist or where the matter that started the universe came from. It is good that our ancestors invented the concept of the supernatural, for we need it if we are to answer such questions.

While the physical scientist has not been able to dispense completely with the concept of the unexplainable or supernatural, he has at least managed to consign it to a corner of his mind where it does not greatly interfere with his day-to-day activities. He accepts as "given" the laws and particles of nature and spends little time worrying about the metaphysical problems associated with their origin. However, *he accepts absolutely nothing else as given*. He conceives of the world of physical and chemical phenomena with which he deals as a completely orderly and lawful world, with every detailed event, whether it be the formation of a new galaxy or the fall of a raindrop, being the effect of causes which are themselves the effects of other causes, and so on, going back ultimately to the fundamental particles and the basic laws of the universe. Even the existence among his laws of a principle of indeterminacy limiting the precision with which the future can be predicted does not permit the entry of caprice into the world of the physical scientist. Within a calculable and frequently very narrow range of uncertainty, the future is completely determined by the past. Given the laws and the particles, all else follows inexorably.

It is a measure of how far the modern world has come that few who read the preceding paragraphs will find either strange or objectionable the ideas expressed there—as long as they are clearly understood to relate only to the properties of inanimate matter. But when it comes to biological science, a different situation exists. There is by no means universal agreement on the extent to which living organisms resemble nonliving matter in having structure and properties determined entirely by the operation of immutable and unchanging natural law. Many are convinced that there is a basic difference between biological and physical phenomena in the degree of their ultimate scientific explainability. And even those who believe generally in the validity of natural law in biology may still feel that the laws applicable to living matter differ in profound essentials from those which control nonliving matter.

In former periods it was not difficult, even for practicing scientists, to employ entirely different philosophies when interpreting biological and physical phenomena. There were obviously vast differences between living creatures and inanimate objects. The overall properties of reproduction, growth, purposive behavior, adaptability, and the like just did not exist in the world of the physical scientist. And even when the structural and functional details of living organisms were investigated, the conspicuous features were found to be complex organs, nervous systems, tissues, and cells that seemed to have no nonbiological counterparts. Since the biologist possessed the normal human genetic endowment, he could not help looking for cause/effect relationships, or "natural laws," to help explain the complexities with which he had to deal in terms of a smaller number of simpler concepts. In this he was partially successful, but his laws, dealing with such things as the response of living organisms or parts of living organisms to environmental change, had little resemblance to the comparatively simple and mathematical relationships the physicist was steadily establishing among his particles and forces. Biology and physics appeared to be entirely separate fields.

The biologist, with subject matter incomparably more complex than that of the physicist, had an even greater need for recourse to the supernatural to bolster the underpinnings of his science. For this purpose the particles and laws of the physical scientist did not seem to be relevant. Instead, there appeared to exist underlying purposive and directive forces in living organisms of a quality lying completely beyond the reach of cause/effect considerations. The terms "vital force" and "vitalism" were coined to represent the many aspects of the phenomena of life that, it was believed, would never be susceptible to scientific explanation.

There was a certain tidiness about the clear cleavage between biology and physics, each possessing its own separate sphere of action and each governed by its own religious dogma. Such separation also had the great advantage of consistency with one of the most humanly compelling of all philosophic tenets—the anthropocentric notion placing man above and beyond the workings of natural law designed for the regulation of an impersonal world. For the idea of the fundamental irreconcilability of life processes with the principles of physical science has always been a popular one almost automatically accepted as true, at least until proved false by overwhelming evidence.

Nevertheless, with the growth of knowledge both in the physical and the life sciences, the neat separation between the fields became difficult to maintain. Despite the essential convictions of practicing scientists, biology and physics had a tendency to come together. In retrospect, it seems more than coincidental that the event generally considered to have launched biology as a true science—Harvey's discovery in 1628 of the circulation of the blood—consisted of a demonstration that ordinary principles of hydraulic engineering could be successfully applied to explain a vital function of the human body.

In the 350 years since Harvey's discovery one after another of the aspects of biology that were originally believed destined to be eternally dependent upon the mystery of vitalism for their explanation has been moved out of the realm of the supernatural by the application of the ordinary laws of physical science. Not only the gross functions of the body organs but many of their details of structure and operation have been found amenable to explanation by the methods of the physicist and chemist. Even the substances that go into the composition of the tissues and cells of living organisms have been found to owe their architecture and properties to the operation of the same physical laws of atomic particles and forces that govern the chemistry of nonliving matter.

In short, the coalescence of the physical and the life sciences has progressed so far that many scientists in both disciplines now suspect that there is no fundamental difference between them— that ultimately *all* aspects of the structure and behavior of living matter will be explainable in terms of exactly the same fundamental particles and natural laws as those underlying the load-carrying qualities of a bridge, the flight capabilities of a rocket-ship, or the color of a sunset. According to this magnificently unifying concept, there is but one ultimate science, and that is the science of the physicist.

But if there is only one ultimate science, there must also be only one ultimate supernatural, and that must consist in its totality of the postulate of the original existence of the fundamental particles and natural laws of physical science. All else in biology, as well as in physics and chemistry, must follow. Since living matter is only a different manifestation of the operation of the same particles and natural laws as those governing nonliving matter, there can be no "vital principle," "vital force," or "vitalism" that pertains to the one but not to the other.

These thoughts, of course, are not new. The Greeks formulated many of them. But there is something about the context in which they arise in the twentieth century that is significantly different from that of previous eras. The thesis of the possible unity of all science emerges today, not just from the contemplative mind of the philosopher, but from the laboratory of the scientist. In the twentieth century this is no longer merely one of many competing theses, all similarly unverified and seemingly unverifiable. Instead, we are now confronted with an unbroken path of scientific discovery, extending back several hundred years, each successive step of which moves closer to what has for some time seemed to many to be an inevitable ultimate conclusion. What was once Greek philosophy has become a scientific hypothesis worthy of objective consideration and treatment by the techniques of the scientific method.

I have dealt with some matters related to the probable unity of science in an earlier work.* In terms of the loose categories that we popularly apply to the functions of higher animals, the subject matter there treated was "mental" rather than "physical." In that area it seemed to me that the evidence was rather convincing that all aspects of complex behavior and intellectual activity will ultimately find satisfactory explanations in terms of the purely physical laws of nature. Although it was harder to do, I thought it was even possible to reconcile the subjective phenomena of personal awareness with the concept of the reign of the natural laws of physical science in the domain of human experience.

Obviously, even if it had been entirely convincing, the earlier treatment could not have been considered a complete demonstra-

---

* Dean E. Wooldridge, *The Machinery of the Brain* (McGraw-Hill Book Company, New York, 1963).

tion of the ultimate identity of biology and physics. For it remained to be shown that the so-called physical properties of living organisms could also be expected to arise by the normal workings of the laws of physics. To complete my statement of the case for the unity of science, I have written the present book. In effect, its subject matter consists of the accumulated evidence for the essential continuity between nonliving matter and living organisms. Insofar as the evidence is convincing, the age-old "mystery of life" is indeed exposed as a clever, but essentially nonmagical, trick of the ordinary laws of physics.

My treatment is intended to be reportorial, not creative. I attempt no new ideas; instead, I try to describe past discoveries and current developments that are pertinent to the modern thesis of the essential continuity between nonlife and life. I do not try to hide my own opinions and prejudices—I believe in the ultimate reducibility of biology to physics. Nevertheless, I do try to tell the story as objectively as possible so that the reader can form his own conclusions. It may be that some who read this book will end, as well as start, with a conviction in the essential soundness of the vitalistic philosophy. If so, this outcome will be perfectly understandable both to those readers and to me. To them it will be a consequence of the weakness of the case developed for the physical interpretation of the phenomena of life; to me it will be a tribute to the objectivity of the presentation.

Let us proceed now to a brief historical review of some of the early developments that set biology on a converging course with physical science.

part 1

*Physical Nature
of the Components
of Living Organisms*

chapter 1

The Major Parts
of the Living Machine

In the twentieth century it is not easy to comprehend the views
that prevailed a few hundred years ago as to the nature of life
and living creatures. Then as now every person, every day of his
life, was bombarded by evidence for the orderly operation of
cause and effect in biological phenomena. If the body was cut
with a knife, blood would flow; if food was long withheld,
weight would decrease; if the nostrils and mouth were tightly
closed, death would result.... Nevertheless, in the nonscientific
intellectual climate that prevailed during the Middle Ages, such
clear-cut evidence that living creatures, like inanimate objects, are
controlled in at least some aspects of their behavior by regular
natural laws had little effect on popular ideas about biology.
Vitalism in its most extreme form governed whatever thought
there was on the subject. Living creatures, and especially humans,
were thought to lie outside the realm of subject matter suitable
for investigation and understanding; life and the living body

13

were believed to be replete with mysteries that must forever lie beyond the comprehension of mortal man. Not only was it therefore hopeless to try to make careful observations and deductions on life processes, it was also, in some dark and frightening way, wrong to do so. Magic potions and incantations were employed to combat disease and injury, not just because nothing better was available but also because such techniques were clearly best suited to deal with the nonphysical mysteries believed to underlie the afflictions under treatment.

It is likely that the gradual emergence of biology as a field of study and activity appropriate to its name—the science of life— would have commenced many years earlier than it did had it not been for the retarding effect of the mystical belief in an unbridgeable chasm separating animate and inanimate processes. Nevertheless, a start was finally made. It came in the early 1600s, when William Harvey made his observations and put forth his deductions upon the movements of the heart and blood.

While every schoolboy learns that William Harvey discovered the circulation of the blood and became famous thereby, it is not commonly appreciated why this seemingly obvious and simple discovery was so important as to entitle Harvey to be called "the father of modern biology." Harvey's great fame rests on two bases, one of his own making and the other a philosophic consequence of his discovery. Harvey's first claim to fame was based on the thoroughly scientific method he employed in arriving at his conclusions. Not only did he study all the books and reports of the anatomists who had preceded him (unsound though many of them were), but he performed a long series of experiments of his own. He dissected and minutely described what he saw in dogs, pigs, serpents, frogs, fishes, slugs, oysters, lobsters, and insects. He watched fluids circulating in the transparent shrimp and the unhatched chick. He traced the arteries and veins of animals and men and studied the positioning and functioning of valves in both heart and blood vessels. He actually calculated the capacity of each ventricle and estimated the resulting rate of flow of the blood. He observed the results of obstructing the flow of blood in selected arteries and veins and performed other experiments to test his theories. In short, Harvey employed the same sequence of careful observation, hypothesis formation, testing of hypothesis by new observation, and modification of hypothesis to fit the new data that describes all modern scientific research. In the early seventeenth century this was unique in biological investigation. It was a tremendous departure from the mixture of unsupported speculation and religious mysticism that had permeated the work of most of Harvey's predecessors.

Although the introduction into biology of the scientific method was accomplishment enough to justify Harvey's fame, the philosophic implications of his discovery were probably even more important to the future of biology. For Harvey had shown that ordinary physical laws—in particular, those governing the pumping and flow of liquids—were capable of accounting for the functions performed by the heart, an organ that had previously clearly belonged in the realm of the unknowable. Harvey's explanation of the properties of the circulatory system constituted the first important evidence that the principles of physical science were relevant to at least some of the processes underlying the phenomena of life.

It would carry us too far afield to trace in detail the historical development of understanding of the functions of the various organs of the body that has followed the pioneering work of William Harvey. Suffice it to say that faith in the hypothesis that such functions can be understood through the application of the principles of physics has not led to disappointment. In addition to our knowledge that the heart is a pump, we now know that the lungs comprise a mechanism for the introduction of oxygen into the body's chemical plant and for the extraction of gaseous waste products; we understand a great deal about the digestive processes in the stomach and intestines; we can follow the transport of oxygen, food, and waste products by the blood; the chemical purification activities of the kidneys and the liver are pretty well detailed; the glandular secretion of hormones and their resulting stimulation of specific chemical reactions in remote organs of the body are no longer the mystery they once were.

The validity of our understanding of the functioning of the organs of the body is evidenced by spectacular recent developments in surgery. The employment of heart/lung machines to substitute for the natural organs during lengthy operations on the respiratory or circulatory system is one modern example. The surgical implantation into the body of battery-powered electronic pulse generators that supplement the inadequate muscle-contracting capabilities of a defective heart is another. The artificial-kidney machines, which prolong indefinitely the lives of patients with defective kidneys by periodic chemical removals of the accumulated impurities in the blood, are yet another example of the success of the mechanistic approach to body function. Most spectacular of all are the strides being taken toward the development of techniques for the transplantation of organs into human patients from other humans or animals. Despite the great difficulties occasioned by the body's rejection mechanism, which causes a chemical reaction that frequently attacks and destroys organic transplants from other individuals, the medical literature now includes numerous reports of successful transplants of kidneys from one human to another. Patients have even lived for weeks after the implantation of kidneys from monkeys to substitute for their own nonfunctioning organs. There have been lung transplants in humans. During the preparation of this book there appeared a report attesting to the current state of good health of a Brooklyn puppy more than six months after its heart had been replaced by a transplant from another, unrelated dog. There is at least one case on record of the transplantation of a heart in a human patient dying from failure of his own organ. Unfortunately, a human heart was not available for transplantation, and the heart of a monkey had to be used. It was inadequate and the patient died, but not for an hour or so. From the viewpoint of the patient the operation was clearly unsuccessful, but as an indication of the essential soundness of the modern understanding of the functions of the body organs, even the temporarily successful operation of a human's circulatory system by the heart of a monkey must be considered to be an important accomplishment.

In a book such as this, dedicated as it is to an inquiry into the adequacy of the purely physical laws of nature for explanation of the properties of living organisms, the successful interpretation of the functions of the body organs in terms of machinelike processes is of the greatest significance. Our twentieth-century familiarity with current medical events such as those just cited can easily blind us to their philosophic importance. We should not forget that, before the thread of development initiated by Harvey's pioneering work on the circulatory system, there was general belief in the essential inapplicability of physical principles to body processes. Today the popular point of view is entirely different. With the possible exception of "mental" activities, most of us now would subscribe to the thesis that the essential functions of the parts of the body are all ultimately understandable in terms of the same physical laws that govern the operation of inanimate machines.

This removal from the essential functions of the body organs of any claim of dependence on nonphysical explanation, important though it is, is only the first of many steps we must take if we are to attain the goal of a physical interpretation of all life processes. As our next step, let us consider the materials out of which living organisms are constructed and inquire whether nonphysical, vitalistic principles are needed to account for their existence and properties. We shall commence by going back in history and tracing the development of understanding of the similarities and differences between *organic* and *inorganic* matter.

chapter 2

The Basic Construction Materials

Even the medieval alchemists had noted that there were two general classes of materials. Materials of the one class remained essentially unchanged after being heated and then allowed to cool. Salt would glow red hot, lead would melt, water would vaporize —but on being cooled each material would revert to its original appearance and properties, evidently none the worse for wear. It was entirely different with materials of the other class. Sugar would char when heated and would not regain its original condition when cooled. Olive oil, like water, would vaporize, but, unlike water, it would not return to liquid on cooling. Eventually it was noted that the heat-resisting materials were of inanimate origin, coming directly from the earth, air, or sea; on the other hand, the materials that were easily modified or destroyed by heat all seemed to derive from living organisms. In the early 1800s the two classes of substance were given the names *inorganic* and *organic,* respectively.

In this determination by observation of the existence of two

19

classes of materials and the adoption of labels for their convenient identification the method was scientific and the logic unassailable. Unfortunately, at this point the leading scientists of the day concurred in a not very scientific guess, and they guessed wrong.

"Guess" is not precisely the word to describe the mental exercise in question here—what the scientists did was in effect to update and reaffirm the old idea of the essential mystery and unknowability of the life processes. The success of Harvey and his followers in explaining the functions of the organs of many animals in purely physical terms made it impossible, at the start of the nineteenth century, to retain a vitalistic doctrine as all-embracing as that of previous eras. Nevertheless, it was still possible to postulate a vitalistic chasm separating the *materials* of living organisms from those of inanimate objects. This was done: the doctrine was put forth that there exists an unbridgeable gulf between inorganic and organic matter—that the ordinary physical laws which might be expected ultimately to explain the construction and properties of the one could never account for the construction and properties of the other. In particular, a mysterious "vital force," it was held, was involved in the formation of organic matter. Since this force lay completely beyond the reach or comprehension of the chemist, there was no way that organic materials could be made except Nature's way—by the mysterious workings of Life in the bodies of plants and animals.

But even this more restricted, materials-oriented doctrine of vitalism was in for a rough time. As early as 1827 a discovery was announced that rendered it at least partially untenable. There was a trace of irony in this development, for the instrument for the event, a German chemist named Friedrich Wöhler, was a former pupil of the Swedish chemist Jons Jakob Berzelius, whose great authority and prestige had been responsible for the wide acceptance of the vitalistic theory of materials in the first place.

In modern terms Wöhler's epoch-making discovery seems ridiculously simple. He put two well-known inorganic chemicals in a test tube, gently heated the mixture, and found the result to be an organic substance. The initial inorganic ingredients were ammonia and cyanic acid, while the organic end product was urea, a common animal waste product.

It was no easier 140 years ago than it is now for a young scientist to find the courage to report a finding that completely contradicted the longstanding convictions of his elders. Therefore, Wöhler proceeded cautiously in developing his conclusions. Four years elapsed between his original experiment and his final publication, during which time he repeated the experiment many times and devised many chemical tests of his raw materials and end product to ensure that his interpretation was correct. Finally, there could be no doubt about it. Although his published paper was written in more formal terms, its essential claim was colorfully stated in a letter Wöhler wrote to Berzelius: "I must now tell you that I can make urea without calling on my kidneys and indeed without the aid of animal, be it man or dog. Ammonium cyanate is urea."

Of course, one robin does not make a spring. Urea might have been some kind of rare exception, not really typical of organic matter. But it wasn't. In 1838 Wöhler and a collaborating chemist, J. von Liebig, reported the synthesis from inorganic ingredients of no fewer than sixteen additional organic substances. By the middle of the nineteenth century, dozens of organic substances had been created in the chemist's test tube.

In addition to these important experimental successes in the changing of matter from one form to another, the nineteenth century saw rapid progress in the growth of basic understanding of the science of chemistry. Such fundamental knowledge was to be of overriding importance in the determination of the ultimate fate of the materials-oriented doctrine of vitalism.

The chemists, for example, came to realize that the thousands of different substances occurring in nature were composed of only a few dozen different kinds of fundamental construction materials. These basic ingredients of ordinary matter were isolated and identified by a variety of new techniques. For example, it was found that electricity passing through water tore the water apart into two colorless gases, which were known as hydrogen and oxygen. But these ingredients could not be further broken down into simpler materials. If either of them were tightly confined and protected from contamination by other materials, it could be heated, cooled, compressed, subjected to ultraviolet light, electric discharge, or any other kind of torture that could be invented by the chemist without any perceptible effect on its properties—it would remain the same colorless gas, would still combine with the other gas under the proper conditions to form water, and so on. One of the principal preoccupations of the nineteenth-century chemists became the invention of methods of breaking down familiar substances into their seemingly fundamental and indestructible components and determining how many different types of such components could be isolated and identified. These basic ingredients of matter, like hydrogen and oxygen, were named *elements*, while the more complex substances which could be broken down into two or more different elements were called *compounds*.

The chemists soon were able to identify and determine the properties of a few dozen elements that seemed able to form an almost limitless variety of chemical compounds by combining in various proportions. Nitrogen was another colorless gaseous element like hydrogen and oxygen but with different combinatorial properties (thereby entering into the formation of different compound substances). Carbon was a black, sooty material. Sulfur was a yellow, solid element that burned in air with a blue flame and produced a distinctively acrid gaseous product as a result. And so on.

From the point of view of our present interests the importance of these developments is that organic and inorganic substances were found to be composed of the same elementary construction materials. The sugars, starches, fats, and oils manufactured in living plants and animals were found to consist simply of carbon, hydrogen, and oxygen bound together in various definite proportions. The albuminous substances, later to be called proteins, also contained substantial amounts of nitrogen, together with smaller quantities of other elements such as sulfur and phosphorous. And the same basic chemical elements, bound together in different proportions, made up all the inorganic substances of earth, air, and sea.

Such discoveries, of course, were entirely compatible with the experimental demonstrations of Wöhler and others that organic substances could be synthesized from inorganic ingredients. Common construction materials were used. If the chemist could rearrange these materials by heating the inorganic compounds, shining light on them, passing electricity through them, or by doing any of the rest of his growing bag of tricks, there seemed to be no reason, in principle, why an "organic" arrangement of the construction materials could not result. Apparently, at least in special cases, it did. In these instances there was certainly no unbridgeable chasm between inorganic and organic matter. If a vital force principle, residing outside the domain of natural law, was involved in the construction of living matter, it could not be involved in *all* the ingredients of animate organisms. It seemed clear that a vitalistic doctrine of material construction, to survive, would at least have to introduce its nonphysical principles at a higher level of organization of matter than that corresponding to simple organic compounds.

Thus the logical next step for our investigation to take must consist of an inquiry into more complex organic compounds than the simple ones we have treated so far. But before we can take such a step, we shall have to devote some attention to the structure, as well as the ingredients, of organic compounds.

BIBLIOGRAPHY

Asimov, I., *The Intelligent Man's Guide to Science* (Basic Books, Inc., Publishers, New York, 1960), chap. 10, "The Molecule."

Asimov, I., *The Wellsprings of Life* (Abelard-Schuman, Limited, New York, 1960), chap. 11, "Building Blocks in Common."

Moore, R., *The Coil of Life* (Alfred A. Knopf, Inc., New York, 1961), chap. 4, "Wöhler and Liebig: Makable by Man."

chapter 3

The Biological Building Blocks:
The Simpler Organic Molecules

The early-nineteenth-century discovery of the identity of the elemental building materials appearing in inorganic and organic
matter and of the resulting intertransformability of the two classes
of substance did not, of course, invalidate the original observations that essential differences exist between the *properties* of substances of inanimate origin and those of substances normally created by life processes. It was still true that organic matter was in
general less stable—more vulnerable to heating and other disruptive treatment—than the compounds possessing an inanimate
heritage. It was equally true that two houses could have entirely
different architectural properties even though both were constructed of exactly the same kinds of lumber, concrete, flagstone,
and tile. It had yet to be discovered how, in chemical compounds
as in houses, the proportions and detailed arrangements of the
building materials could be as important as their elemental prop-

erties in determining the characteristics of the resulting structure. Insight into the important relations between the construction details and the resulting properties of aggregations of matter was provided by the development of an understanding of the nature of the structural units of the construction materials—the *atoms* of which the elements are composed.

The inadequacy of our terminology causes us, in the mid-twentieth-century, still to speak of the "atomic theory of matter," despite the fact that the word "theory" conveys to nonscientists an impression of tenuousness that is completely belied by the breadth and depth of support for the pertinent concepts that have by now been established. Our near-certainty of knowledge about the basic features of the atomic construction and properties of matter is today not far different from our near-certainty that the sun will rise tomorrow morning; each near-certainty arises from the combined effects of many observations made by many people over long periods of time. For example, we now know that the gaseous element hydrogen consists of units, or atoms, the most important characteristic of which is that each atom contains a heavy nucleus with a positive electric charge surrounded by a much larger and lighter region of negative electricity. We know that, in its normal state, the positive charge on the nucleus is electrically balanced by the extranuclear negative charge. We know, further, that the element helium has a nucleus that possesses exactly twice the positive charge of the hydrogen nucleus and is correspondingly surrounded by an ambient cloud of exactly two units of negative electricity. The light metallic element lithium has three units of charge on nucleus and surrounding "electron cloud." The beryllium atom has four units of charge, boron five, carbon six, nitrogen seven, oxygen eight, and so on. We know now that the chemical properties of the elements are entirely determined by their configurations of extranuclear electric charge.

Hydrogen, helium, nitrogen, and oxygen are gases (at ordinary temperatures) because the electric forces between nearby atoms are not such as to immobilize the atoms in a rigid solid configuration; lithium, beryllium, boron, and carbon are solids because their nuclear and extranuclear distributions of electric charge lead to forces that do greatly restrict the freedom of movement of the individual atoms. The light-absorbing and -reflecting properties of an element, and therefore its color, are determined by the detailed interactions of the extranuclear cloud of negative electricity with incident rays of light. The chemical combining properties of an element with other elements are determined by the same detailed configuration of electric charge and the resulting ease or difficulty with which the negative clouds of the combining atoms can rearrange themselves into a stable pattern that surrounds and at the same time holds together the nuclear components.

This development of understanding of the atomic nature of matter, which has progressed without interruption since the English chemist John Dalton suggested in 1803 that all matter is made up of tiny, sub-submicroscopic particles, has made of chemistry a science rather than an art. But in the process the science of chemistry has turned out to be fundamentally indistinguishable from the science of physics. The fact that a mixture of hydrogen and oxygen gases combines to form water, when heated to a certain temperature, may appear at first glance to be a purely chemical observation far removed from the considerations of forces, fields, attractions, and repulsions of the physical scientist. But the difference disappears when the chemical process is analyzed more deeply and found to be only a manifestation of the operation of forces of electric attraction and repulsion among the positively charged nuclei of hydrogen and oxygen and their surrounding negatively charged electric clouds. Even temperature is found to be only another term for the average speed with which the randomly moving gaseous particles bump into one another, thereby influencing the rate of the resulting "chemical" reaction.

In a treatment such as this one, concerned with the thesis that living organisms are subject to the same laws of nature as those which determine the properties of inanimate objects and man-made machines, it would have been awkward if the essential identity of the laws of chemistry and physics could not have been established. Although it remains to be seen whether the same set of laws is sufficient for the explanation of biological phenomena, we would clearly be wasting our time if it were still thought, as it used to be, that chemistry and physics are distinct fields of science with separate governing principles.

But we have digressed. The present discussion has as its aim the development of certain concepts bearing on the construction and properties of inorganic and organic compounds. To this point we have explicitly dealt with the electrical nature of both an atom of an element and the forces that permit atoms of more than one element to bind themselves together in a stable configuration by redistributing among themselves the clouds of negative electric charge that each isolated, neutral atom normally possesses. Such a stable combination of two or more atoms is, of course, a *molecule* of a chemical compound. Just as the atom is the indivisible building block of an element, so the molecule is the building block out of which a compound is composed. Two atoms of hydrogen bound together with one atom of oxygen form a molecule of water. Again, this is not simply formal terminology. The properties we associate with water—its liquidity, wetness, colorlessness, freezing and boiling characteristics, and all the rest—are determined solely by the detailed spatial configuration of positive and negative electric charge automatically established when 1 oxygen and 2 hydrogen atoms join together.

The implications are similar when we speak of 1 nitrogen and

3 hydrogen atoms combining to form a molecule of ammonia, of 1 silicon and 2 oxygen atoms combining to form quartz, and so on. These are inorganic substances. Chemical formulas can similarly be specified for organic substances. Historic urea, for example, is a compound with a molecule consisting of 1 atom of carbon, 4 atoms of hydrogen, 1 atom of oxygen, and 2 atoms of nitrogen. Glucose, an important sugar that is formed in most living organisms, has for its molecule 6 atoms of carbon, 12 of hydrogen, and 6 of oxygen. A molecule of morphine, another organic substance that was analyzed not long after Wöhler synthesized urea, contains 17 carbon atoms, 19 hydrogens, 3 oxygens, and 1 nitrogen. At about the same early period, the strychnine molecule was found to be made up of 21 atoms of carbon, 22 of hydrogen, 2 of oxygen, and 2 of nitrogen.

From the foregoing paragraph, the alert reader will have noted a curious point: every organic molecule referred to possesses more atoms than any of the inorganic molecules described. Is this accidental, just the result of inept choices of illustrative examples by the author, or does it mean something? The answer is that it means something. From the very origin of analytic techniques permitting the determination of atomic constitution it was found that inorganic molecules were typically much less complex than molecules of animate origin. To be sure, there was a sort of continuity: unusually big inorganic molecules that were more complex than unusually small organic molecules could be found. Nevertheless, the strong general rule was that the one kind of molecule was made up of only a few atoms, the other kind of many.

There is another important characteristic of organic molecules related to the element carbon. Here again, the examples we have cited are typical: carbon is not an especially common ingredient of inorganic compounds; it is almost always a constituent of organic material. Thus, before the middle of the nineteenth century it was apparent to the chemists and biologists that life processes tend to produce large and complex molecules and that these molecules usually contain many carbon atoms.

While quantitative differences in composition may seem less important than clear-cut qualitative differences, in this case their magnitude is impressive. In carbon content, for example, 48 percent of the dry weight of the human body consists of this element, compared to only about 0.03 percent in the surface layers of the earth. And the difference in complexity between organic and inorganic molecules can be as large or larger. Molecules composed of many thousands of atoms are commonplace in living organisms; a half dozen or so atoms make up even the most complex of the inorganic molecules. Could it be that the success of Wöhler and his followers in synthesizing the simpler organic materials from inorganic components was not the major accomplishment that it appeared to be, that there does indeed exist an unbridgeable chasm between different classes of chemical substances but that the position of the chasm is further up the line toward the gigantic carbon-based molecules of living organisms rather than at the boundary between what we have defined as organic and inorganic matter? It is fair to say that such a doctrine of modified vitalism did not have a great deal of currency even in the late nineteenth century—by that time most chemists and biologists were convinced that the properties of all molecules, large and small alike, would ultimately be explained in terms of the same set of physico/chemical laws. However, the prominent role played in life processes by mammoth carbon-rich molecules was worrisome. Until progress could be made in the analysis and synthesis of these peculiarly organic particles, it could not truly be said that the essential identity of the laws underlying the properties of all the molecules of living and nonliving matter had been established.

Many of the largest organic molecules, which also seem to be of the greatest importance in life processes, belong to a class of substances that has been named protein. Our narrative carries us next to a consideration of protein molecules and the extent to which the physically based principles of chemistry have been found capable of explaining their properties and their formation.

BIBLIOGRAPHY

Asimov, I., *The Wellsprings of Life* (Abelard-Schuman, Limited, New York, 1960), chap. 12, "The Shape of the Unseen."

Morowitz, H. J., *Life and the Physical Sciences* (Holt, Rinehart and Winston, Inc., New York, 1963), chap. 2, "Atoms and Cells."

chapter 4

The Building Blocks
"of First Importance":
Protein Molecules

Before the end of the eighteenth century the attention of chemists had been attracted to a group of organic substances that behaved in an odd manner. These substances, upon being heated, changed from liquid to solid, rather than the other way around. The white of eggs, a component of milk, and a substance in the blood were early identified as having this property. These materials were also found to be similar in a number of other respects. In particular, they were found to consist principally (though not entirely) of carbon, hydrogen, oxygen, and nitrogen and to contain approximately (though not exactly) the same percentages of these elements in their composition. Because of certain early clues as to its key importance in vital processes, this strange class of substance was named *protein* (from the Greek, meaning "of first importance").

There has never been cause to regret the choice of the term "protein." To begin with, protein substances are found in all living organisms. In the human body, for example, proteins are easily identified in all the tissues and organs. They are also essential in the food we eat. Higher animals can survive quite well on diets that are almost entirely protein (plus a few vitamins), but carbohydrates, fats, oils, and vitamins alone will not sustain life. If there is any one class of substance that deserves to be called the "stuff of life," it would appear to be protein.

Although the techniques available to the early-nineteenth-century chemists permitted them to measure the relative amounts of the different elements in proteins, the determination of the molecular compositions of proteins was quite another matter. The evidence did suggest, however, that molecules of protein were much more complicated than those of any other known substances. Indeed, as early as 1839 the Dutch chemist G. J. Mulder proposed a formula for a protein molecule consisting of 40 atoms of carbon, 62 of hydrogen, 12 of oxygen, and 10 of nitrogen. His formula was wrong: it was not nearly complicated enough!

While the early attempts to work out precise formulas for protein molecules were doomed to failure by the great complexity of the substances, there was another line of exploration that did lead to useful results. To appreciate the significance of this successful trend of development, we must bear in mind that "protein" does not refer to one specific substance, as "urea" does, for example. Instead, it is the name for a class containing a very large number of different substances. For example, there are probably tens of thousands of different protein substances in the human body alone. All possess such points of similarity as complexity of molecular structure and approximate proportions of the elements carbon, hydrogen, oxygen, and nitrogen. But the differences are important too, not only in the *precise* proportions of the constituent elements but in gross physical properties as diverse as those of muscle fibers and digestive juices. The impressiveness of the work we are about to consider rests, in fact, on these great differences in the appearance and properties of different proteins. For the nineteenth-century chemists discovered that, despite such differences, all proteins are constructed of molecular components of only a few standardized types.

A French chemist, H. Braconnot, took the first important steps toward an understanding of protein construction. As early as 1820 he put some *gelatin* (a protein obtained by boiling animal gristle) in a dilute acid and applied heat to see what would happen. One result was that, after prolonged heating, there appeared some sweet-tasting crystals, which ultimately came to be called *glycine* (from the Greek word for "sweet"). In a later experiment, by heating muscle tissue in acid, Braconnot isolated another crystalline substance, this time tasteless and white in color, which he called *leucine* (from a Greek word for "white"). Some years later the German chemist J. von Liebig obtained a third crystalline substance by heating a milk-curd cheese in an alkaline solution; this was called *tyrosine* (from the Greek word for "cheese").

Glycine, leucine, and tyrosine were interesting both for their differences and their similarities. Glycine was sweet, but leucine and tyrosine were not; glycine was quite soluble in water, leucine only slightly soluble, tyrosine practically insoluble. Yet each was extracted from an animal protein, each formed crystals, each exhibited acidic properties when in solution, and each would release ammonia when suitably treated. Because of the last two properties—acidity and ammonia content—the three substances came to be known as *amino acids*.

As the years went by, other crystalline substances were obtained from proteins. All were found to possess properties entitling them to be called amino acids. Evidence also accumulated that the amino acids, which may have been obtained by heating a protein in hydrochloric acid, for example, were not formed by chemical recombination of smaller fragments into which the protein might have been torn by the action of the hot acid. Instead, it was ultimately established that the amino acid molecules were intregal structural elements of the larger protein molecule; the hot-acid treatment seemed to soften the "mortar" that held them in place and thereby permit them to fall out of the structure, but it did not affect the integrity of the amino acid components themselves.

The discoveries went further. Not only were molecules of the amino acids structural units of protein molecules, but they were found to be the *only* structural units involved. Complete analysis of protein material, when it finally could be carried out, showed that it consisted of nothing except amino acid molecules. And, despite the discovery of tens of thousands of different kinds of proteins, it was found that they employ only 20 different amino acid components! It must be emphasized that these components are completely standardized. Glycine, leucine, tyrosine, and all the rest, can be obtained out of human protein, whale protein, bat protein, trout protein, snail protein, dandelion protein, or bacterial protein. The tyrosine from one is identical with the tyrosine from all the rest, and so on for the remaining amino acids.

The determination that the tremendously varied class of proteins—the most typically "organic" of all materials—employs only a handful of basic structural units was rendered even more spectacular by the later discovery that these units greatly resemble one another in their molecular structure. When chemical techniques permitted the determination of the detailed spatial relationships of the atoms in a molecule, it was found that all amino acid molecules have similar "backbones." Each backbone consists of 2 carbon atoms, 2 hydrogen atoms, 1 oxygen atom, and 1 nitrogen atom arranged in a standardized three-dimensional configuration that is stabilized by the cohesive forces produced by the sharing of electric charge among the adjacent atoms.* The chemical and physical properties distinguishing one amino acid from another were found to be due to the attachment, always at the same spot of this basic backbone, of one of 20 distinctive "side chains" of atomic configurations. The unique properties of glycine were found to be due to the simplest possible side chain —one hydrogen atom. The leucine side chain consists of a characteristic spatial arrangement of 4 carbon and 9 hydrogen atoms; the tyrosine side chain contains 7 carbon atoms, 7 hydrogens, and 1 oxygen; and so on.† But, different though the side chains and the resulting chemical properties of the different amino acids are, the backbones are all the same—always the same three-dimensional arrangement of 2 carbon atoms, 2 hydrogen atoms, 1 oxygen atom, and 1 nitrogen atom.

Befitting the structural utility of the amino acids, the backbone was found to have an important property: because of the natural chemical forces resulting from its configuration of electric charge, one end of the backbone of one amino acid molecule has a strong affinity for the opposite end of the backbone of another amino acid molecule. Thus, amino acid molecules have a tendency to form long linear arrays by hooking together end to end. Such an array constitutes a protein molecule. The specific kind of protein formed in each case is determined by the specific sequence of

---

* The formula given here applies to an amino acid constituent of a protein molecule. An isolated amino acid segment in aqueous solution attaches an extra hydrogen ion to one end and an OH ion to the other, to achieve its acidic properties. When two amino acid segments link together in protein formation, these attachments are cast off in the form of a molecule of water.

† For some amino acids the side chain contains more atoms and is bigger that what we have called the backbone. Thus it is not necessarily correct to think of an amino acid molecule as a long, narrow structure.

amino acid molecules in the linear array. The evidence is that every molecule of a given protein type contains exactly the same number and kinds of amino acid molecules, arranged in exactly the same order, as every other protein molecule of that type. Since each protein molecule may contain hundreds or even thousands of amino acid components and the properties of the protein may be changed if only one of these many components is altered, there exist almost limitless possibilities for variety in protein materials. The number of possible combinations of the 20 basic structural units in an average-sized protein molecule of 500 amino acids is approximately 10^{600}—a 1 followed by 600 zeroes!

Although the sophisticated details of protein chemistry lie well outside the scope of this book, it would be unnecessarily misleading to leave the reader with a description of a protein molecule characterized by a very long, thin, array-type structure. Such a stringlike view of the protein molecule is correct only if we remember that strings have a tendency to get twisted and tangled. Modern evidence indicates that this is true of protein molecules. The long string of amino acids of which each molecule is composed twists and turns upon itself so as to produce a three-dimensional tangle. The tangle is not random or accidental, however. The specific twists and convolutions of the backbone * of one molecule are just like those of another of the same protein. The electric forces produced by the side chains that protrude from the main backbone result in detailed attractions and repulsions that cause the array to fold and twist upon itself in a definite, characteristic way. Thus, while the protein molecule is a tangled ball of string, the tangle is designed, not haphazard. As we shall see later, the chemical properties of the resulting mole-

---

* The backbone of the protein molecule consists, of course, of the sequence of segments composed of the backbones of the linked amino acid molecules.

cule upon which vital processes of living organisms depend are largely determined by the detailed three-dimensional configuration of electric fields produced by the specific pattern of twisting and folding of the linear array.*

We started this chapter with the avowed intention of ascertaining whether protein materials, like simpler organic substances, could be accommodated in a nonvitalistic philosophy based on an assumption of continuity and essential similarity between inorganic and organic matter. The most convincing answer to the question would be a demonstration that proteins, like urea, can be fabricated in the laboratory out of inorganic materials. We now have the background needed for intelligent consideration of this important question: Can proteins be synthesized?

Because the answer to the question is to be something less than a categorical yes, we should start by paying a bit of attention to the difficulties that confront the chemist in working with these giant molecules. Although we have written glibly about the composition and molecular structure of the various amino acids, the number and arrangements of amino acids in a given protein molecule, the patterns of twists and folds of the linear array, and the like, each of our assertions could be made only because of literally hundreds of man-years of laboratory effort by brilliant and dedicated chemists. And it has been easier for them to arrive

---

* Two structural principles go a long way toward accounting for the specific conformations assumed by protein molecules. To begin with, the long-chain molecule has a strong tendency to form a helix—always of the same diameter and pitch—which permits the electric charges on the amino acid segments on adjacent turns of the helix to fit together. However, the side-chain construction of two of the twenty kinds of amino acid—*proline* and *hydroxyproline*—is not conducive to such bonding. Therefore, at points where these amino acid components occur in the protein molecule, the helix must make a sharp bend. The resulting succession of straight helical segments separated by sharp bends leads to the kind of tangle envisioned in the preceding discussion.

at general properties of proteins than to determine the detailed structure of specific protein molecules. Despite ultracentrifuges, electron microscopes, X-ray spectrometers, artificially radioactive tracer materials, paper chromatography, and all the other modern devices and techniques that aid the chemist today, the sheer complexity of the giant molecules of living organisms renders almost impossible the task of analysis, let alone synthesis. In fact, it was only in 1958 that F. Sanger, of England, was awarded a Nobel Prize for working out the first complete sequence of amino acids in a protein. It is significant that the protein he chose to work on was *insulin,* whose molecule contains only 51 amino acid components. By comparison, the *hemoglobin* molecule, which is of average size for proteins, contains more than 600 amino acids!

In the mid-1960s, therefore, when we are just becoming able to analyze the detailed composition of some of the simpler proteins, it is too early to report great success in their synthesis. However, important progress has been made. Amino acids have been synthesized from inorganic ingredients. And amino acid molecules have been hooked together to form chains or arrays. This, by the way, is not quite as easy to accomplish as might be suggested by the earlier reference to the strong tendency of the backbones of these molecules to hook together. Perhaps an analogy can be drawn with a zipper. The opposing sections of the zipper are designed to fit together tightly, but energy has to be supplied by the slide fastener to bend the two sections a bit and force them into the correct spatial relationship before the closed, stable configuration can be achieved. So it is with amino acids. The energy whereby the front end of one backbone is forced into the proper relationship with the back end of the next is usually supplied chemically by temporarily hooking on to one end of each amino acid an energy-rich molecule. This molecule (or the pieces into which it may have broken during the reaction) drops away from the structure after it has provided the motive power for linking the two amino acids together.

Early techniques whereby the chemist laboriously linked one new amino acid at a time to a slowly growing chain have been supplemented by more recent methods whereby chains of hundreds of or even a thousand amino acids can be formed rapidly in the test tube. These synthetic chains are comparable in size with moderate-sized natural protein molecules, and they prove, under test, to have many proteinlike properties. Nevertheless, it cannot quite be claimed they are the same as naturally formed protein. For, owing to limitations of the techniques of synthesis, they are usually made up of only one or two of the 20 different kinds of amino acids. Apart from a few simple proteins, such as *fibroin* in silk, nature appears not to employ such a monotonous architectural design for its giant molecules.

Thus it is correct to say that we cannot yet synthesize most natural proteins, and for two reasons: our analytic techniques are usually not yet good enough to permit us to determine the amino acid sequence in the natural protein molecule with the precision required to provide a blueprint for its construction; and even if we possessed the necessary blueprint, our techniques of synthesis are usually not yet good enough to permit us to assemble hundreds or thousands of the different kinds of amino acid molecules in the precisely specified order. Nevertheless, following Sanger's work, complete structural determination *has* been made of a dozen or so natural proteins. Furthermore, a few proteins *have* been synthesized in the laboratory—either small in molecular size or of unnatural monotony of architecture, to be sure, but nonetheless proteins. The problem of protein synthesis has clearly been solved in principle, even though the detailed complexity of the task is often more than current techniques can cope with.

In later chapters we shall make the acquaintance of another

class of giant molecules that play an important role in living organisms—the *nucleic acids*. We shall learn how recent developments make it clear that the nucleic acids are, along with proteins, "of first importance" in vital processes. Therefore it is pertinent to note, at this point, that the important conclusions we have reached in this chapter about proteins also apply to the nucleic acids. Like those of proteins, molecules of nucleic acid are long chains possessing a backbone of repetitive segments, with chemical individuality of the segments conferred by side chains. As in proteins, only a few different kinds of structural unit—backbone segment plus side chain—are combined in different sequential order to yield a bewildering variety of giant molecules. As in proteins, the structural units can be synthesized from inorganic matter, and they can then be hooked together in the test tube to form nucleic-acid-like molecules. Again like proteins, the man-made article falls far short of nature's in complexity and variety.

It is important that we have a clear understanding of the lesson that is to be learned from the nineteenth- and twentieth-century developments in the analysis and synthesis of proteins and the similar but more recent developments pertaining to the nucleic acids. It is simply this: Abundant evidence now exists that the structures and properties of the most complex of organic molecules, as well as of the simple ones dealt with a hundred years ago by Wöhler and others, are in principle completely understandable in terms of the laws of physics. An atom of an element is composed of nothing more than the fundamental particles of the nuclear physicist, held together by the nuclear and electric forces described by his laws of physics. A small molecule consists of nothing more than a few such atoms, held together by the forces arising from the sharing of their extranuclear electric charge. The physical and chemical properties of a small molecule are also completely determined by the specific distribution of electric charge in and around the molecule. A large molecule consists of nothing more than an aggregation of smaller molecules, which fit together the way they do only because of the mutual forces of attraction and repulsion deriving from their arrangements of electric charge. When a large molecule twists, turns, and tangles the linear array of which it is basically composed into a complex three-dimensional form, it does so under the precise control of the same forces of attraction and repulsion that arise out of the detailed distribution of electric charge along the backbone and side chains of its array. The resulting chemical and physical properties of the large molecule, be it protein or nucleic acid, are also no more and no less than the resultant of the effects of the detailed three-dimensional distribution of electric charge trapped and held within its tangled web. Fantastically complicated though a large protein or nucleic acid molecule may be, the problem its structure and properties pose to human understanding is one of degree, not of quality. A simple molecule of water, with its 1 oxygen and 2 hydrogen atoms, brings into play exactly the same and as many basic natural laws as a molecule of the protein *excelsin,* which contains approximately 40,000 atoms!

Thus, more than a century after the synthesis of urea by Wöhler, the demonstration that he commenced has finally been completed: there is no need for invoking any special vital principle to account for the structure and properties of any of the chemical compounds found in living organisms. This, of course, does not of itself prove that a nonphysical, vital force does not exist in life processes. However, if such a force does operate in biology, it is now clear that it must come into play in one of two ways: it can enter into the determination of properties that appear only when molecules are grouped together in living organisms, or it can influence the mechanisms whereby in nature, as distinct from in the laboratory, the complicated molecules essential to life are in fact produced. We shall defer consideration of the evidence for or against the operation of vitalistic principles at higher levels of organization of matter. For our next exercise we shall attempt to employ the established laws of physics and chemistry to devise a plausible explanation for the formation in nature, before the existence of living organisms, of the complex molecules on which life depends.

BIBLIOGRAPHY

Asimov, I., *The Genetic Code* (The Orion Press, Inc., New York, 1962), chap. 4, "The Building Blocks of Protein," and chap. 5, "The Pattern of Protein."

Asimov, I., *The Intelligent Man's Guide to Science* (Basic Books Inc., Publishers, New York, 1960), chap. 11, "The Proteins."

Asimov, I., *The Wellsprings of Life* (Abelard-Schuman, Limited, New York, 1960), chap. 11, "Building Blocks in Common," chap. 12, "The Shape of the Unseen," and chap. 13, "The Surface Influence."

Haurowitz, F., *The Chemistry and Function of Proteins* (Academic Press Inc., New York, 1963), chap. 7, "The Internal Structure of Globular Proteins."

Herskowitz, I. H., *Genetics* (Little, Brown and Company, Boston, 1962), chap. 32, "Biochemical Genetics (II)."

Moore, R., *The Coil of Life* (Alfred A. Knopf, Inc., New York, 1961), chap. 17, "Pauling and Sanger: The Proteins—Another Coil."

Morowitz, H. J., *Life and the Physical Sciences* (Holt, Rinehart and Winston, Inc., New York, 1963), chap. 4, "Large Molecules."

part 2

The Natural Chemical Origins
of Simple Lifelike Organizations of Matter

chapter 5

The Paleontology of Protein

In a curious way, all that we have learned to this point about the structure and properties of the complex molecules of life has not yet invalidated the original vitalistic dogma that organic matter can be created only by living organisms. To be sure, chemists can now manufacture organic material, but are not chemists alive? There is a serious point here: the susceptibility to a purely physical interpretation of the structure and properties of an existing complex organic molecule is by no means proof that the many thousands of atoms it contains could ever have been arranged in just that form through the unaided operation of natural law in an inanimate world. If the first American astronauts to set foot on the moon were to find there a message in Russian scratched on its surface, their ability to hypothesize a series of meteoritic impacts capable of producing just the observed configuration of scratches would hardly be likely to convince them that it really happened that way. And in our case, are we really to believe that the blind workings of the ordinary laws of physics, without the intervention of some nonphysical, vitalistic guiding principle, can account for the architecture of the precisely specified, fantastically complicated protein and nucleic acid molecules?

What we are about to do is to reopen one of the most impassioned controversies in the history of science—the question of spontaneous generation. To be sure, we don't quite stir up this major philosophic issue just by suggesting that natural processes may have been capable of building organic molecules out of inorganic material. For no one contends that a molecule of protein, for example, is of itself alive. But obviously we are not going to stop there. If we can establish a reasonable and purely physical hypothesis for the origin of the complex molecules of living matter, we are going to try to push our arguments along to account for the ultimate and completely automatic organization of these molecules into living forms. At that point, if we reach it, we shall clearly be coming into conflict with the position held by practically all scientists for a hundred years, a position that was eloquently stated by Louis Pasteur during a public-demonstration lecture at the Sorbonne on April 7, 1864:

And, therefore, gentlemen, I could point to that liquid and say to you, I have taken my drop of water from the immensity of creation, and I have taken it full of the elements appropriated to the development of inferior beings. And I wait, I watch, I question it!—begging it to recommence for me the beautiful spectacle of the first creation. But it is dumb, dumb . . . for Life is a germ and a germ is Life. Never will the doctrine of spontaneous generation recover from the mortal blow of this simple experiment.

We are about to take the first steps along a path of scientific exploration that, after a century, is proving Pasteur to have been wrong.

The question we must treat in this chapter can be simply stated: "Before life existed on earth, how could protein molecules have been formed?" Since the rules of the game we are playing require that we have recourse only to the ordinary laws of physical science for our hypotheses, we must obviously start by inquiring into the physical conditions of the primordial earth at the time of interest. Considerable progress has been made in astrophysics and paleogeology in recent years. Certain speculations are now believed to be pretty safe with respect to the conditions existing on earth several billion years ago, before the development of plants and animals. For example, we can be sure there was little if any free oxygen in the atmosphere of the preanimate earth. This is because oxygen reacts so readily with the minerals that compose the major bulk of the earth, and is so scarce with respect to those minerals, that it would all be taken up by chemical combination in a few thousand years if there were no continuing supply of free oxygen. Today the source of supply is plant life, which releases oxygen into the atmosphere at such a rate as to maintain a 20 percent relative concentration of this element in the air, despite its tendency to combine with materials of the earth's crust. Before the existence of vegetation, however, there was no way that free oxygen could be maintained in the earth's atmosphere.

Hydrogen, on the other hand, must have been relatively abundant in the primordial atmosphere. This element is known to comprise more than 90 percent of the mass of the universe. To be sure, the light weight of the hydrogen molecule renders this gas unusually susceptible to escape from the earth's gravitational field, so it is likely that there was a gradual depletion of this element after the original formation of the earth some five billion years ago. Nevertheless, calculations suggest that appreciable quantities of hydrogen still remained in the atmosphere, three or four billion years ago, when the events we are about to consider took place.

Other important constituents of the primeval atmosphere must have been gaseous compounds of hydrogen and other relatively abundant elements, such as nitrogen and carbon. These gases would include *methane,* CH_4, and *ammonia,* NH_3. Water vapor must also have been present, the result of evaporation of water from the earth's surface. The arguments for this kind of atmospheric composition are not entirely speculative. These gases are known to be prominent in the atmospheres of the other planets of our solar system. Jupiter, Saturn, Uranus, and Neptune, as well as some of their satellites, contain methane in their atmospheres. Ammonia is present on Jupiter and Saturn. Hydrogen is found on all.

In the preanimate era, as now, a major part of the earth's surface was covered by oceans. The average temperature was higher than it is now, thereby facilitating chemical reactions, but not high enough in the period of interest to boil and vaporize the ocean waters.* There was more volcanic action than we have today, and this produced local hot spots with their attendant enhanced chemical activity. Turbulence in the air produced by the volcanic eruptions resulted in extensive electric discharges that disrupted the atmospheric gases and aided the recombination of the resulting molecular fragments into new and sometimes more complex forms. The radioactivity in the earth's crust was also many times greater than it is now. The consequent bombardment of chemical compounds by high-energy nuclear particles resulted in a higher rate of decomposition and recombination of atomic and molecular fragments than we would observe today. Ultraviolet radiation from the sun beat upon the surface of the earth with an intensity that today would destroy most modern forms of life because of the extensive chemical activity that it was capable of inducing. This was not because the sun emitted more

---

* This limitation would still have permitted ocean temperatures much higher than what we now consider to be the boiling point of water if, as seems likely, the atmospheric pressure was many times greater than it is today.

ultraviolet radiation in those days; rather it was because of the absence of the shielding ozone layer, about twenty miles up, that today absorbs the most energetic of the rays before they can produce their lethal effects on the living things that inhabit the surface of the earth. This shielding layer of ozone—a special molecular form of free oxygen—was absent in primeval times because it, like the more customary form of free oxygen, can be maintained in the atmosphere only by the action of countless billions of living plants.

These, then, were the essential conditions: an earth largely covered by warm water; an atmosphere largely composed of water vapor, methane, ammonia, and hydrogen; and a substantial rate of chemical activity in the earth's surface and atmosphere resulting from intensive bombardment by radioactive particles, extensive lightning discharge, brilliant ultraviolet illumination, and local regions of high temperature. Was there anything in this set of conditions that was conducive to the formation of organic molecules?

At first glance, the situation does not look promising. While the conditions were favorable for the breaking down of the simple inorganic molecules in the seas and atmosphere into smaller fragments, it is hard to see how this would result in recombination of the fragments into the complex structures characteristic of the kinds of matter we have called organic. On the other hand, our understanding of the chemical effects of the laws of physics in situations of this nature is not detailed enough to permit us to predict, with confidence, just what would be the results of exposing the specified ingredients to the postulated environment. An experiment might seem indicated. Why not prepare a mixture of the gases believed to have constituted the primeval atmosphere, subject it to one or more of the kinds of energy believed to have been important at the time in question, and see what happens? An obvious experiment? Yes, but if, as seems likely, the result of such an attempt should be negative in the sense of not producing detectable quantities of organiclike molecules, what would it mean? After all, nature had several billion years to perform *its* experiment; what would be the significance of a failure to obtain positive results in a laboratory experiment lasting only the few weeks or months that would be practicable for this kind of exercise?

Discouraging though the prospects appeared, the attempt had to be made. Interestingly enough, it was not made until 1952. In that year S. L. Miller, a graduate student at the University of Chicago, circulated a mixture of water vapor, ammonia, methane, and hydrogen past an electric discharge (to simulate the ultraviolet radiation of the sun). He continued this process for only one week. Nevertheless, when he analyzed his mixture at the end of the experiment, he found unmistakable traces of "organic" compounds, including several of the amino acids!

The unexpected success of Miller's relatively simple experiment naturally inspired others to undertake similar investigations. It was soon learned that Miller's results could be duplicated and extended. Some of the most important results were obtained by the University of California chemist Melvin Calvin. (Some of Calvin's work actually preceded Miller's discovery, but in his earlier work ammonia was not present so that nothing as complex and significant as amino acids had been observed.) Calvin employed high-energy electrons, rather than ultraviolet radiation, as his source of disruptive energy. Using the facilities of the Lawrence Radiation Laboratory at Berkeley, he was able to simulate the kind of electron bombardment that might have resulted in primordial times from the natural disintegration of one of the radioactive elements. When a mixture of water, methane, ammonia, and hydrogen was subjected to the high-energy electrons and then analyzed for new ingredients, a veritable storehouse of complex molecules was discovered. In addition to amino acids of several kinds, there were sugars, fatty acids, hydroxy acids, urea, and even several of the bases that, as we shall learn later, play in the nucleic acid molecules a component role similar to that played by the side chains of the amino acids in protein molecules. In short, Calvin's experiment yielded an impressive number of the different kinds of molecular units employed in nature in the construction not only of proteins but also of carbohydrates, fats, oils, and nucleic acids—the essential materials of living organisms!

The results of Calvin and Miller have been repeated and extended by other experimenters. It has been shown that a methane-ammonia-water mixture, heated to high temperatures such as would have been occasionally produced by meteoritic impact in the primordial atmosphere, produces at least 14 of the 20 amino acids that occur in living organisms. And ultraviolet irradiation at cool temperatures of a mixture of water and *hydrogen cyanide* —a compound that is frequently formed in experiments such as those of Miller and Calvin—has been found to result in two of the key nucleic acid bases. Similar treatment of mixtures of water and *formaldehyde*—another common product of the experiments —has produced the two sugars that are found in nucleic acid. In short, it has by now been demonstrated that almost any kind of input to a suitable atmosphere of energy—whether from heat, ultraviolet, electric discharge, or radioactivity—will synthesize the building blocks of life's molecules.

Of course, it should not be imagined that the *only* new ingredients produced by the irradiation or bombardment of a "primeval atmosphere" are those which are essential to the construction of organic molecules. In Calvin's work, for example, there were in addition a number of other molecular products, not all of which were completely analyzed. However, the important point is that, when the simple molecules of water, ammonia, methane, and hydrogen believed to have comprised the major part of the primeval atmosphere are torn asunder by electric discharge, heat, radiation, or radioactive bombardment, an appreciable fraction of the resulting fragments automatically recombine into just the kinds of molecules that have turned out to be the basic structural units of all living matter.*

Although such experiments convincingly establish the point that we need in order to get on with our task of reactivating the doctrine of spontaneous generation, it is hard to avoid a digression at this point to consider a troublesome question. Why do things work out this way? Why should amino acids, for example, just happen to have been among the prominent products formed when the primeval atmosphere was disrupted by the naturally existing forces of heat, lightning, ultraviolet radiation, and radioactive bombardment? There is an answer to this question. In physico/chemical terms, there are various stable configurations of carbon, hydrogen, oxygen, and nitrogen atoms. Their mutual electric forces of attraction and repulsion are such that, if atoms of the four species are brought near one another and jostled about by the effects of external sources of energy, they will tend to stick together in one or another of these stable three-dimensional arrangements. Depending upon the accidental details of atomic juxtaposition and jostling, the result may be one or another amino acid, a sugar, a nucleic acid base, or an inorganic molecule.

Such an explanation may convince us of the prosaic inevitability of the early formation of amino acids, but it is not likely thereby to suppress our tendency to feel that there is still some-

---

* In experiments such as those described, the variety of organic building blocks produced was, of course, limited by the starting ingredients used. In a real primeval atmosphere there would be traces of sulfur, phosphorous, sodium, potassium, and other elements that would presumably permit the formation of amino acids and other organic molecules with side chains including these materials.

thing peculiar going on here. Granted that amino acids had to be formed out of the inevitable workings of the laws of physics on the atmospheric ingredients of the preanimate world, how did it happen that they were just the structural units needed for the construction in nature of the very special kinds of giant molecules that, a billion or so years later, contributed to the appearance of the remarkable new phenomenon of life? This question, too, has a nonvitalistic answer. It is epitomized in the assertion that modern organisms are based on amino-acid-containing substances because they constitute a class of long-chain, complex molecular material that happened to be *available* in the primordial earth, not because they were uniquely *required* for the creation of life. As we move along into aspects of our treatment in which the principles of evolution and natural selection come into play in the development of the progenitors of living organisms, we shall encounter no reason to believe that the specific kind of chemistry of living matter that we have on earth today is the only kind of chemistry that could support life. The results obtained by Calvin and Miller seem mysterious only if we imagine that the only form of life possible is that which we know, which is so strongly dependent on just the kinds of products that they looked for and found in their experiments. The mystery vanishes if instead we imagine that there are various possible molecular components on which life might be based, that among them are those found in the experiments and presumably therefore generated in the atmosphere of our preanimate earth, and that natural processes of evolution and selection (yet to be treated) did the rest.

But let us resume our speculation on the natural origins of proteins. To this point our picture is essentially that of the gradual formation of amino acids and other organic structural units by the action of electric discharge, heat, ultraviolet radiation, and high-energy radioactive particles on the gaseous ingredients of the atmosphere. These new substances, being heavier than the atmospheric gases, gradually rained down into the seas beneath. With the passage of time, the accumulation of this organic material steadily increased until, after a billion years or so, the seas that covered most of the surface of the earth became what someone has vividly described as a "hot dilute soup."

The next step in the natural formation of protein material had to be the linking together of amino acid molecules into chains. We have seen that the backbone of each amino acid molecule has a structure that permits such linking, but we have also learned that, in the laboratory at least, it takes more than just stirring together a mixture of amino acids to cause chains to form. Specifically, energy has to be supplied to force the successive links of the chain together before they will lock in a stable configuration. In the artificial synthesis of protein that was discussed earlier, the necessary energy was supplied chemically, by the temporary attachment of energy-rich substances to the ends of the amino acid backbones. It turns out that there are other ways of doing the trick. For example, if a suitable mixture of amino acids is made hot enough, some of its molecules will have enough energy of motion to cause them to hook together. To be sure, this simple process does not easily occur in water, and probably would have been effective only on dried-out beach sediments. But Calvin has recently described multiple-step chemical reactions, involving a number of the molecular components of the "hot dilute soup," that take place readily in water and include among their products linked chains of amino acid—that is, protein molecules. Similar reaction sequences have also been shown capable of assembling the available ingredients to form other relatively complex organic molecules, including nucleic acids.

It is attractive to think of ponds or lakes, rather than the open sea, as the principal sites of this early chemical activity. Inland pools surely were formed from time to time by local seismic raising or lowering of the land. Evaporation of most of the entrapped water would greatly increase the concentration of the amino acids and other organic constituents in the pool, thereby greatly accelerating their interaction to form more complex substances. Further concentration probably resulted from the known affinity of organic molecules for certain clays and sands, which must have dotted the bottoms and shores of the primeval pools and constituted local gathering points for the active chemicals. If in addition a volcanically produced hot spot happened to be nearby, the resulting combination of high temperature and high concentration would constitute an efficient "factory" for the fabrication of proteinlike material as well as other relatively complex organic substances.

In a qualitative description such as this there is a danger of making everything seem too easy. The processes we have postulated to explain the origin of organic matter seemed, until just the last few years, most improbable. It required such developments as Miller's exciting synthesis of amino acids to raise what had previously been unsubstantial speculation to the status of a respectable scientific hypothesis. Although it has only been hinted at in this treatment, the problem of quantitative sufficiency has also been a difficult one for the theory to cope with. Calculations of the probable concentrations of amino acids and other organic components attained in the vast quantity of ocean water covering the earth, and of the resulting probability of close approach of two or more of the component molecules with just the right thermal energy to cause linking, have always led to rates of generation of organic compounds that would be completely negligible in terms of ordinary time scales. To be sure, factors of thousands in the speed of the reaction can be evoked by such assumptions as those concerning inland pools and local volcanic heating. Nevertheless, in the final analysis the only thing that makes the hypothesis quantitatively tenable is the tremendous period of time that was available for increasing the thickness of the hot dilute soup and sustaining the chemical interactions of the ingredients.

In this connection there at first appeared to be a troublesome problem. Even though organic constituents continually rained out of the primeval sky for a billion years or more, did their concentration in the surface waters continue to increase during all this time? We know that such organic materials would disappear rapidly if put into the ocean today. Fortunately, we also know the reasons for their limited lifetimes, and these reasons were not valid in the preanimate era. Specifically, any constituent of organic matter disappears rapidly today for one of two reasons: it is either eaten by bacteria or it is destroyed by oxidation. Charles Darwin, whose preoccupation with evolutionary phenomena logically compelled him to speculate on the origin of life, stated it well:

It is often said that all the conditions for the first production of a living organism are present, which could ever have been present. But if (and oh! what a big if!) we could conceive in some warm little pond, with all sorts of ammonia and phosphoric salts, light, heat, electricity, etc., present, that a protein compound was chemically formed ready to undergo still more complex changes, at the present day such matter would be instantly devoured or absorbed, which would not have been the case before living creatures were formed.

Defenseless though the components of organic material are against their animate enemies and the destructive effects of the free oxygen produced by living plants, in the preanimate period there appears no reason to question their ability to survive indefinitely, as seems required by the hypotheses we are considering. We may observe incidentally how fortunate it is that evolutionary processes ultimately resulted in different means of production of the materials essential to living organisms. Otherwise, it seems certain that the development of higher life forms would ultimately have been markedly limited by the decreasing availability of the basic ingredients of life arising out of the destructive properties of the new organisms themselves.

But we are getting ahead of our story. The important point is that, with the help of some laboratory results and various hopefully reasonable assumptions, we have developed a fairly strong case for the existence in the seas, lakes, and tidal pools of the preanimate earth of significant concentrations of proteinlike chains of amino acids and of other typically organic materials such as carbohydrates, fats, oils, and nucleic acids. This is not yet "life" as we understand it, but at least it constitutes a group of promising ingredients for use in the further development of our theories. Let us move along to a consideration of whether the operation of the ordinary laws of physical science on these organic ingredients appears capable of accounting for the development of even more lifelike organizations of matter.

BIBLIOGRAPHY

Beck, W. S., *Modern Science and the Nature of Life* (Doubleday & Company, Inc., Garden City, N.Y., 1957), chap. 6, "The Unit of Life."

Calvin, M., *Chemical Evolution* (University of Oregon Press, Eugene, Ore., 1961).

Calvin, M., "Chemical Evolution," *Proceedings of the Royal Society (London), Series B* (to be published, 1965).

Ehrensvärd, G., *Life: Origin and Development* (The University of Chicago Press, Chicago, 1960), chap. 7, "Out of Dust and Fire."

Encyclopaedia Britannica *1965, Book of the Year,* special report on "The Origin of Life."

Oparin, A. I., *The Chemical Origin of Life* (Charles C Thomas, Springfield, Ill., 1964), chap. 1, "Initial Stages in the Evolution of Carbon Compounds," and chap. 2, "The Formation of the Primaeval Broth."

Oparin, A. I., *Life: Its Nature, Origin and Development* (Academic Press Inc., New York, 1962), chap. 2, "The Origin of Life."

chapter 6

The Primeval Lakes:
Giant Precursors
of Living Organisms

We have already found our attention drawn to isolated bodies of water as the probable sites of chemical activity basic to the aggregation of the simplest organic molecular units into more complex forms. We shall find further concentration on these primeval lakes to be profitable; for we have not yet exhausted the possibilities they offer for the development of organizations of matter leading toward life.

There is a question that is sure to bother many readers as we continue to focus attention upon isolated bodies of water as the sites of major events of early chemical history. From what has gone before, it is clear that we are going to speak glibly of processes continuing for many millions of years. Yet geological evidence, at least that pertaining to more recent eras, would hardly justify our assigning a longevity of more than a few thousand years at the most to a typical enclosed body of water. The resolution of this seeming contradiction is one familiar to geologists. It is assumed that the actual sequence of events was an intermittent one: periods of hundreds or a few thousand years of chemical activity in the favorable environment of an enclosed pool were interspersed among dormant periods of hundreds of thousands or millions of years during which the partially developed organic sediments of earlier times were "out of action"—perhaps covered by volcanic material or trapped in the interior of a newly extruded mountain range.* Initiation of new activity occurred when the restless stirrings of the earth's crust exposed some of this material again. Perhaps circumstances then led to the formation of a new lake that dissolved the old deposits and introduced them into a further round of chemical processing; perhaps instead the old organic material, on reexposure, was picked up by the wind or by streams and carried to remote regions, part of it settling in existing lakes and seas and thereby affecting the course of chemical history in these new domains.

Thus, while for simplicity the following discussion will treat the situation as though a typical chemically active body of water had indefinite longevity, the reader must understand that a long series of successive periods of activity and dormancy is in fact implied. The existence of such a pattern of sporadic activity will not affect our argument except to emphasize again that the processes with which we are concerned must have required an extremely long period of time for their completion. Fortunately, the one or two billion years that geologists allow us for these developments is also an extremely long period of time.

In addition to the pattern of intermittency, some other features

* This may well be an oversimplification. It is possible that important steps in the chemical development of complex from simpler organic forms occurred during these "inert" stages—under the influence of heat, pressure, and the juxtaposition of previously processed organic materials.

need to be added to the picture of an organically active lake developed in the preceding chapter. The concentration of the simple organic molecules that rained down from the sky and their ensuing gradual combination into more complex forms is only part of what must have gone on in these ancient chemical plants. There must also have been much activity involving inorganic materials. Dissolved minerals from the lake bed and nearby mountains must have introduced metallic compounds into the water; volcanic gases escaping from the earth's interior must have contributed substantial quantities of *hydrogen sulfide,* H_2S, and *carbon dioxide,* CO_2. Under the accelerating influence of heat from volcanic activity presumably existing near the more interesting early pools, a bewildering variety of chemical transformations must have slowly occurred.

Certain chemical transformations would have had especial importance for the developments that lay ahead. This would have been true, for instance, of reactions resulting in the formation of energy-rich molecules. Very frequently such energy-supplying components are needed to cause small molecules to join and form the larger ones that we know are of major importance in the lifelike structures whose development we are attempting to trace. Reference has already been made, for example, to their role in providing the motive power required to hook amino acids together. It is, of course, unlikely that random interactions in the primitive lakes would have resulted in significant quantities of anything as effective as the *adenosine triphosphate* (ATP) molecules that provide most of the energy for the metabolism of modern organisms. However, some kinds of configurations capable of transferring energy to other interacting substances would have occasionally formed. We shall have more to say later on about such important energy-rich molecules.

Of course, there was nothing very biological about any of this early activity. Most of the transformations yielded compounds that we would regard as uninteresting by-products, in the sense of not contributing to the development of forms of organization of matter pertinent to life. Even so interesting a process as the linking together of several amino acids, for all its pioneering importance, still fell far short of the creation of the gigantic, precisely designed protein molecules of modern times. In the period of which we are speaking, sophisticated molecular architecture could hardly have existed. Countless primitive, protein*like* and nucleic acid-*like* molecules must have been formed, but surely nothing that would be accepted today as suitable construction material by any self-respecting living cell.

With this general view of the "starting conditions," let us see if we can trace some of the early developments that led to the gradual appearance of more complex organic materials. If we had such mobility in time and space that we could go back and determine the chemical composition of, say, a thousand of the primordial pools and repeat the measurements every hundred years, we would soon be struck by a curious circumstance: we would find the pools developing "individualities" of their own. Among the almost limitless number of possible chemical combinations of the simple organic and inorganic constituents present in the pools, we would find that some pools would "specialize" in some of these combinations and other pools would specialize in others. As inquiring scientists, we would then find it necessary to search for a nonvitalistic, purely physical explanation of this unexpected "purposiveness" of behavior of our primitive chemical plants.

A part of the explanation of the growing diversity in the chemical content of the pools would be easy to find: the pools did not all start out alike. Geological and meteorological accidents led to differences in the dissolved minerals, in the continuing supply of volcanic gases, in the concentration of the original atmospherically derived organic materials, in the extent and temperature of local hot spots, and the like. These differences would, by the normal operation of the physically based laws of chemistry, affect the relative probabilities of different possible reactions and thereby, with the passage of time, contribute individuality to the chemical character of the pools.

The development of this degree of understanding would bring us to a critical point in our imaginary investigation. If we were not careful, we would be apt to assume that we had found the complete explanation for the growing diversity in the chemical composition of the pools, and move on to some other aspect of the study. This would be a mistake, for it would cause us to miss an important discovery. If we had just continued our observations for another few centuries, we would sooner or later have stumbled across examples of sudden and dramatic changes in the chemical activity of the pools that could not be accounted for satisfactorily by detectable differences in the reacting ingredients. From time to time a pool would seem suddenly to develop a mind of its own; for it would take off on a new course of chemical activity featured by the rapid generation of complex products that it had previously manufactured in insignificant amounts, if at all. We shall find the explanation of this phenomenon more difficult than the earlier determination of the individuality-contributing effects of the starting conditions of the pools and more rewarding in terms of its contribution to our ultimate understanding of processes important to life.

To develop the important point that is here involved, we must start by talking about the phenomenon of *catalysis*. The phenomenon was first observed in 1822 by the German chemist J. W. Dobereiner. He even incorporated his discovery in a working device—a kind of automatic lighter—in which a jet of hydrogen would start to burn in air without the intervention of a spark or match. All that was necessary, he found, was to direct the unlighted jet against a surface covered with powdered platinum metal. For some reason, mysterious to Dobereiner and his contemporaries, this caused the hydrogen to ignite, that is, to combine spontaneously with the oxygen of the air, which it would not do at room temperature in the absence of the *catalyst,* platinum.

Since Dobereiner's discovery, many substances that catalyze specific chemical reactions have been found. The presence of powdered platinum, nickel, or iron oxide in the reaction chamber is essential in one stage of the preparation of commercial sulfuric acid if the process is to take place at more than a snail's pace. *Copper chromite, vanadium pentoxide,* and *manganese dioxide* also serve as important catalysts in the chemical industry. In fact, much of the success of many industrial chemical processes depends on finding just the right catalyst for the reaction involved.

What does the catalyst do? Well, one thing it does not do is get used up or chemically changed in the reaction it promotes. The same amount of catalytic material, possessing exactly the same molecular configuration, remains at the end of the process as entered the reaction chamber. This is quite different from the result of stimulating a chemical reaction by the kind of energy-rich substance we have previously referred to. Such energy-contributing molecules do not emerge unscathed from the chemical reactions in which they participate. Instead, their molecular structure changes under the influence of the forces set up during the reaction; it is in this way that they provide the additional energy needed to push or pull the atoms of the reacting molecules into their new configurations. But catalysts do not contribute energy to the reacting ingredients; unless suitable energy balance is provided by other means, catalysts are powerless to act. In fact, the catalyst appears not to make possible any chemical reactions that cannot occur in its absence—it just speeds them up. Consider Dobereiner's experiment, for example. In a mixture of hydrogen gas and air at room temperature there will be an occasional combination of hydrogen and oxygen atoms (to form a water molecule), but this does not happen often enough to produce the bulk heating of the mixed gases necessary to sustain combustion. In the presence of platinum the combination of hydrogen and oxygen atoms proceeds so much more rapidly that the gas heats up and bursts into flame.

Much of the mystery that once surrounded the phenomenon of catalysis has been solved. We now know that the catalyst produces its effect by causing the molecules of the reacting ingredients to come into a form of contact with each other possessing a degree of atomic intimacy and precise orientation that would only rarely be achieved in the random, undirected encounters among these molecules in uncatalyzed reactions. In Dobereiner's experiment, for example, hydrogen and oxygen are "adsorbed" onto the surface of the platinum—that is, the interaction of their electric charges with those of the metal is such as to bind the gaseous atoms lightly to the platinum surface. The redistribution of the electric charge of the hydrogen and oxygen atoms resulting from the surface binding turns out to be of such nature as to make it easy for adjacent bound atoms of hydrogen and oxygen to slide together in an intimate configuration that would normally be difficult to achieve because of the shielding effect of the usual arrangement of their extranuclear charge. Once one oxygen and two hydrogen atoms come together on the surface in this way, very strong forces of electrical interaction among them cause further rearrangement of their charge into the stable configuration characteristic of the water molecule. In this process the relatively small interaction forces between adsorbed atoms and platinum are broken, and the new molecule of water escapes from the metal surface, which is then available to perform the same marriage ceremony for the next hydrogen/oxygen arrivals.

In the example given, the catalyst promoted the combination of simpler into more complex chemical forms. Just as frequently, however, catalytic action encourages the breakdown of complex molecules into simpler ones. Iron, for example, will catalyze the reduction of *hydrogen peroxide,* H_2O_2, into water and oxygen. The particular reaction that will occur in any specific situation depends on the details of the interaction among catalyst and starting ingredients and on the workings of the physical laws of chemistry which determine the relative probabilities for the various possible molecular configurations.

It is appropriate at this point to return to our primeval pools and relate what we have learned about catalytic activity to their chemical development. In and among the clays and sands of the lake bottoms it would be natural for some catalytically active metal ores and compounds to be occasionally exposed. Depending upon the specific nature of these materials, one or another class of possible chemical transformations would be selectively encouraged. Because a tiny amount of catalytic material can have a large effect on the speed of a reaction, appreciable contributions to the individuality of behavior of the various pools could result from differences in their catalytic ingredients so small as to be easily overlooked in a not-too-sophisticated survey of the "starting conditions" in the pools.

This is part of the explanation for the temperamental performance we are investigating. For if we eliminate the cases of individuality attributable to inorganic catalysts in the lake beds, we find much more uniformity than before in the chemical behavior of our primordial pools. Nevertheless, some of the most dramatic exceptions to regularity in behavior still persist. A mystery remains to be explained.

Having achieved partial success in accounting for seemingly erratic chemical behavior by recourse to the peculiarly powerful effects of catalysis, let us now look more deeply into this phenomenon in search of additional factors that might have an unsuspected influence on early chemical activity. A clue is provided by modern evidence for the unusual effectiveness of catalysts when they are incorporated in organic compounds. For reasons that are only partly understood, integration into an organic configuration frequently enhances tremendously the efficacy of a simple catalytic substance. It has already been mentioned, for example, that iron catalyzes the breakdown of hydrogen peroxide into water and oxygen. However, if the iron is first incorporated in the compound *catalase,* in which it is chemically combined with a suitable protein and *porphyrin,* another organic substance that occurs frequently in plants and animals, its catalytic effect for the hydrogen peroxide transformation is multiplied 10 billion times!

It is unlikely that large amounts of highly efficient catalysts were present in the primordial pools. However, it seems probable that, in the random, undirected combination of the available molecular components, occasionally a configuration that resulted served as a relatively effective catalyst for a specific mode of linking of some of the other components floating around in the pool. Each such accidentally formed catalytic molecule would then have a sizable multiplying effect on the formation of the related substance. This would account for some sudden, though probably small, changes in the course of chemical development in the pool. However, even more interesting results would occasionally appear.

For suppose that the accidentally formed catalyst we are postulating promotes a chemical reaction whose products include more of the catalyst itself (*autocatalysis*).* The result would be a chain reaction. A small amount of catalyst A would encourage a small amount of the available raw materials to react, yielding a small amount of product B and some more A. The increased

---

* Melvin Calvin of the University of California at Berkeley has emphasized the probable importance of autocatalysis in the chemical developments leading to life.

quantity of catalyst A would cause a second similar, but more extensive reaction. Still more A would lead to still larger reactions, etc. Increases in the rates of formation of A and B by factors of millions or billions could easily ensue. In an efficient autocatalytic chain reaction the runaway acceleration of the chemical activity would probably be limited only by exhaustion of one of the raw materials. Thus, in a few days, weeks, or months,* rather than in the centuries usually required for major changes in the chemical activity of a primordial pool, an apparently brand-new characteristic of the pool could appear, whereby specific types of molecules would thenceforth be formed practically instantaneously (in geologic terms, at least) to the extent permitted by the availability of the necessary raw materials.

In the interest of conveying the essential idea, the above description of the chain reaction has been made unnecessarily narrow. The process need not be as simple as "A catalyzes a reaction which produces more A." Instead, a reentrant chain of multiple reactions may occur. Substance A may catalyze the formation of substance B, which then enters into reactions that rapidly synthesize products C, C', and C'', for example. One of these, say C', may be a catalyst for a reaction yielding substances D, D', and D''. D'', then, may catalyze the formation of E, which finally reacts with available raw materials to produce A, completing the chain. The intermediate products may well include the constituents of carbohydrates, fats, oils, or nucleic acids, as well as inorganic molecules. In a particularly favorable autocatalytic chain, one of the intermediate reactions might even be of a photochemical na-

---

* Even unlimited amounts of the most efficient catalyst would not necessarily produce more rapid, "explosive" reactions. If, as in the processes of most interest to us, energy must be supplied to sustain the reaction, its availability would probably pace the activity. This would be especially likely if the principal source of energy were random thermal interactions with surrounding molecules.

ture, whereby a quantum of ultraviolet light excites one of the interacting molecules and permits the formation of an energy-rich product.* By the participation in the reaction chain of such intermediate products, complex final products possessing a total energy content greater than that of the starting ingredients could be produced. Thus the autocatalytic principle possesses a range and versatility adequate to account for a wide variety of patterns of chemical activity in enclosed bodies of water.

It was in such a manner that sudden and seemingly unpredictable individuality would have developed in the chemical "personalities" of the various primeval pools. Of course, today's scientist would emphasize the point that the diversity of chemical behavior produced by autocatalysis was not fundamentally unpredictable but was instead a consequence of small differences in the starting conditions or previous histories of the pools. Such differences would then account for the sudden appearance, at some stage of development, of a particular kind of autocatalytic chain in one pool rather than in another. This kind of argument is, of course, sound in principle. However, the tremendously large multiplying factors involved in the chemical chain reactions, once started, mean that the differences in initial conditions responsible for substantial differences in the subsequent chemical development of two pools could be almost infinitesimal, lying well below the threshold of detection by "practical" techniques. A most rare and improbable event—the dropping from the sky of a single exotic particle or the fortuitous coming together in the pool of a number of molecules in a particular way that might not again occur in another million years—could get the process started. Thus, the kind of behavior we are describing here would

---

* Such photoelectric effects are known to occur to facilitate many simple chemical reactions, and they should have been much more prevalent in primordial times when the absence of the shielding ozone layer permitted the sun's high-energy ultraviolet rays to bombard the earth's surface.

have seemed to unsophisticated human observers, if there had been any, as clear evidence of nonphysical, vitalistic purposiveness in the behavior of the primordial pools.

The stage we have reached in our narrative—characterized by large numbers of chemically active pools of warm water, each continually receiving supplies of simple organic compounds from the atmosphere, supplemented by inorganic gases and dissolved solids from the earth, with some of the pools exhibiting remarkable efficiency in assembling these available ingredients into more complex organic molecules—represents the total accomplishment towards the development of life achieved during the first one or two billion years of the history of the newborn earth. We still have a long way to go. Let us next concern ourselves with the natural processes whereby the isolated pools of three or four billion years ago may have given birth to the progenitors of the living cells that ultimately became the principal architectural feature of plants and animals.

BIBLIOGRAPHY

Asimov, I., *The Intelligent Man's Guide to Science* (Basic Books, Inc., Publishers, New York, 1960), chap. 11, "The Proteins."

Asimov, I., *The Wellsprings of Life* (Abelard-Schuman, Limited, New York, 1960), chap. 13, "The Surface Influence."

Calvin, M., *Chemical Evolution* (University of Oregon Press, Eugene, Ore., 1961).

Ehrensvärd, G., *Life: Origin and Development* (The University of Chicago Press, Chicago, 1960), chap. 10, "Activity."

Jackson, F., and P. Moore, *Life in the Universe* (W. W. Norton & Company, Inc., New York, 1962), chap. 2, "The Nature and Origin of Living Organisms on the Earth."

Oparin, A. I., *The Chemical Origin of Life* (Charles C Thomas, Springfield, Ill., 1964), chap. 3, "The Origin of the Earliest Organisms," and chap. 4, "The Further Evolution of the Earliest Organisms."

chapter 7

Miniaturization of
The Primordial Pools:
Progress toward Living Cells

Shake a mixture of salt and water and, if there is not too much of it, the salt will soon disappear—dissolved in the water. But shake a mixture of water and an oily substance and something quite different occurs. The oil does not dissolve and disappear; instead, it forms droplets dispersed throughout the water. This tendency toward the formation of droplets is not confined to oils, nor is shaking always necessary to elicit the phenomenon. Substances of large molecular weight—proteins, for example—will spontaneously aggregate to form discrete droplets in water. These spontaneously formed droplets are called *coacervates* (from a Latin verb meaning "to heap up"). They have recently been the focus of considerable attention by those concerned with reconstructing the history of the development of life. A. L. Oparin, for example, a Russian biochemist and pioneer in the field, has emphasized the suitability of coacervates for a major role in the development of preanimate organizations of matter.* For one thing, the droplets can form even though the initial water mixture contains only a tiny proportion of the large-molecular-weight ingredients. For another, the droplets frequently exhibit impressive stability, maintaining their structural integrity despite considerable agitation and mechanical stress. Finally, and perhaps most importantly, the molecular electric forces which lead to the formation of a droplet in the first place frequently contribute to its spherical surface the properties of a selective or *semipermeable* membrane—certain kinds of molecules can pass through the surface, but other kinds cannot; special molecular types may even move through the surface more readily in one direction than in the other. These properties, when taken in conjunction with other physical and chemical characteristics of droplets, probably caused coacervate formation to have a major effect on the course of chemical development in the primordial pools.

Let us consider the consequences of coacervate formation in an early lake of high chemical activity—one in which extensive catalytic processes had developed and a considerable range of organic and inorganic products had been formed. We would expect that some of the coacervate droplets would contain a mixture of many of the various substances indigenous to the pool. Although the surrounding membrane would hold the mixture together, the kind of selective permeability just described might still permit some degree of molecular transfer between droplet contents and surroundings. A very simple kind of membrane selectivity, for example, would permit small molecules to pass through the droplet surface in either direction but make it difficult or impossible for large molecules to do so. Consider the consequences of such a property. As the droplet floated around in the water it would en-

---

* Oparin deserves credit for anticipating many of the modern ideas as to the history of life. A number of the concepts of this treatment were expressed by him as early as 1922.

counter large numbers of amino acid molecules, nucleic acid bases, the even simpler organic constituents of carbohydrates, fats, oils, and other forms of energy-rich molecules, as well as inorganic molecules of hydrogen sulfide, carbon dioxide, and the like. All these molecules, being comparatively small, would pass through the surface membrane into the interior of the droplet. There they would be exposed to a relatively high concentration of the catalysts whose large molecular weight contributed to the formation of the droplet in the first place. This would cause some of the entering material to combine into the more complex molecular configurations of simple proteins, carbohydrates, fats, oils, and nucleic acids. And, of course, autocatalysis would result in an appropriate addition to the store of the enabling catalysts themselves. But the new molecules, being too large to pass out through the semipermeable membrane, would remain trapped in the droplet. Thus the droplet would tend to grow. We can even regard the processes involved as a primitive form of metabolism: "food," in the form of a simple organic and inorganic molecules floating around in the pool, is taken into the droplet through its surface membrane, or "skin"; the food is transformed into more complex organic material; the newly formed complex material enlarges the droplet, causing "growth." We can even add an excretory function to our list. For probably not all the raw material passing into the droplet from the outside would be employed in the catalyzed chemical activity; the remainder, possibly supplemented by small-molecular-weight by-products of the reactions, would represent the "excrement" or "waste material" and would be passed out of the droplet through its surface membrane.

What would be the ultimate consequence of the growth process? That would depend largely on what happened to the membrane as the droplet grew. To this point we have been able to ignore certain complications related to the formation of the surface of the droplet. When the material enclosed within the surface contains not just one kind of heavy molecule but a mixture of different kinds of relatively complex substances, then the normal operation of the physical forces that control the interaction of molecules will almost inevitably cause a certain separation and organization of the contents of the droplet. Specifically, some of the ingredients will tend to concentrate in the interior where they are not in close contact with the surrounding water, while other materials, because of the electrical structure of their molecules, will have a strong tendency to be found on the surface in intimate contact with the water. It is this second class of material that determines the membrane properties. In the specific example we are considering, the droplet requires an adequate supply of a kind of material that is capable of forming a surface of suitable porosity—permitting admission of the "food" molecules from the outside but not permitting escape of the complex products of metabolism. If the catalyzed chemical reactions underlying the growth of the droplet were deficient in their rate of production of such membrane material, growth would be limited—the droplet would fall apart when the available membrane substance would no longer stretch to cover the increasing contents. If, on the other hand, the products of the reactions included too high a proportion of membrane substance, the surface layer might ultimately become too dense and impermeable, thereby shutting off the supply of food to the growing droplet and placing an upper limit on its attainable size.

In addition to such internal effects, there would be various environmental factors that could influence the growth process. Agitation of the water could be expected frequently to break up large droplets into smaller ones, much as we can emulsify an oil/water mixture by severe shaking. Changes in temperature, in the abundance of the inorganic ingredients supplied by volcanic activity or erosion, in the supply of the atmospherically generated organic components—these and other natural events could profoundly speed up or slow down the metabolism of the coacervates. Nevertheless, under suitable conditions these droplets *could* survive and grow.

Once their internal chemical processes included reactions resulting in appropriate catalysts for the synthesis of complex molecules out of simple ones at ordinary temperatures, these new bundles of chemical activity would have been free from any necessity for fortuitously neighboring volcanic hot spots. At the same time, the remarkable enhancement of the concentration of the catalysts and other large-molecular-weight products, made possible by the confining membrane, would have resulted in a rate of chemical activity in a typical droplet that was tremendously greater than that in the pool from which it came. The activity and relative self-sufficiency of the coacervates must have had a far-reaching consequence: they were capable of survival in the open seas! And there would have been many opportunities for members of the new rugged species to reach the ocean waters. The coacervates would in effect be "weaned" from their incubating pools and swept into the great outside world whenever a pool drained to the sea by stream or river, or when a seismic cataclysm reunited a smaller body of water with a larger one.

Once in the open sea, there was nothing to prevent these new and improved droplets from growing (although perhaps more slowly, because of the lower concentration of nutrients). Ultimately, the large droplets, by the normal operation of the laws of physics related to weight, size, and surface tension, would tend to break up into smaller ones. Probably most of the new smaller droplets would lack a mixture of ingredients properly balanced to support growth, and "death" would ensue: continuous wear and tear would ultimately destroy such inert units and return their contents to the sea. But occasionally some of the new smaller droplets would escape from their disintegrating parent with a mixture of catalysts and other substances of proportions that would sustain growth. This would amount to a form of "reproduction" of the coacervates!

Are we to regard these primitive droplets as the first single-celled living organisms? If so, we have come a very long way in support of our thesis that biological phenomena are completely explainable in terms of the ordinary laws of physical science. For the coacervates are clearly nonvitalistic. At no point in our reconstruction of the almost incredibly slow developments that finally culminated in these curiously lifelike bags of chemicals have we had to invoke any nonphysical principle. Yet we have been inexorably led to forms having typically biological properties. The coacervates eat and eject waste products; they exhibit metabolic processes that possess a certain degree of chemical complexity; they grow; they reproduce their own kind; they die. If they are not living organisms or at least progenitors of living organisms, then nature would appear to have played an unusually malicious joke on the modern scientist who attempts to understand his biological heritage. The belief in the straightforwardness of nature that underlies all scientific research must impel us to continue along the path of speculation that has brought us successfully to the present point. We must next address ourselves to a consideration of how physical principles resulted inevitably in natural selective forces that have been given the name *evolution* and how the evolutionary processes operated to accomplish the gradual development of ever-more-lifelike aggregations of matter.

BIBLIOGRAPHY

Jackson, F., and P. Moore, *Life in the Universe* (W. W. Norton & Company, Inc., New York, 1962), chap. 2, "The Nature and Origin of Living Organisms on the Earth."

Oparin, A. I., *The Chemical Origin of Life* (Charles C Thomas, Springfield, Ill., 1964), chap. 3, "The Origin of the Earliest Organisms."

Oparin, A. I., *Life: Its Nature, Origin and Development* (Academic Press Inc., New York, 1962), chap. 2, "The Origin of Life."

chapter 8

Evolution

The time is three or four billion years ago—one or two billion years after the earth was formed. The scene is the open sea; it covers most of the earth's surface, just as it will continue to do for eons to come. The principal characters are the coacervates: small, membrane-enclosed bags of organic and inorganic compounds, including catalytic substances that contribute a high level of chemical activity to what would otherwise be inert, uninteresting drops of oily material. The plot, like that of all good dramatic productions, is based on conflict. Indeed, only a small fraction of our initial cast of characters will survive to the end of the play; the rest must die.

Despite the superficial similarity of the coacervates, the conflict is essentially a struggle among different "species." A particular series of reactions that happened to develop in primordial pool number 543 resulted in the formation of droplets of chemically active compounds of adequate stability to work their way to the open sea and there continue their metabolic processes. But a substantially different set of reactions had occurred in pool number 279, and this had led to injection into the ocean of an essentially different species of coacervate. Similarly for pools 59, 176, 798, and all the rest. The tremendous variety of combinations permitted by the basic versatility of organic and inorganic substances had resulted in a correspondingly wide variety of species among the initial cast of characters in the drama we are about to consider.

As befits the relatively simple nature of the members of the cast, the issue that sets them into conflict is a simple one—food. Initially the problem is not serious, for only a few coacervate individuals are widely scattered throughout vast expanses of ocean. Under these circumstances their ability to grow and reproduce their kind is essentially limited only by their own internal chemistry and a level of concentration of organic and inorganic nutrients in the surrounding water that is insignificantly influenced by the existence of other coacervates. Eventually, however, all this changes. A time comes when the absorption by the growing coacervate population of the nutrients of the ocean is extensive enough to start cutting down on the density of the available food. It is then that the interspecies conflict begins in earnest. For those types of coacervates that have the most effective metabolism, in the sense of being able to assimilate the available nutrients to grow and reproduce most rapidly, then begin to starve the less hardy species out of existence.

From the beginning of the conflict, the tactics employed by the successful species are designed to make effective use of the numerical superiority they achieved in the fast-growing early years, while there was still enough food for all. When the era of overpopulation sets in, the continued eating and proliferating of these hungry hordes cause matters to go rapidly from bad to worse, and what started as a minor recession in the coacervate economy quickly becomes a disastrous depression. Of course, all species are affected by the growing food shortage, for each faces extinction if its birth rate falls below its death rate. And this can occur, be cause the decreasing availability of food curtails the birth rate more than it does the death rate. Ultimately, the small and undernourished coacervate droplets of a slowly growing species must get broken up by agitation, collision, and wear, with their contents spilling into the sea to provide food for the more hardy types.

Thus the plot becomes clear. As our imaginary play continues for the millions of years that must elapse between opening and final curtain, the abundance of nutrients gradually decreases and the less prolific species, one by one, become extinct. At this point we can foresee the final outcome of the drama—the ultimate triumph of the strong over the weak, the emergence from the herd of the species possessed of the qualities most suitable for survival. We may as well anticipate the ending, quit the theater, and reflect on the meaning of what we have seen.

Obviously, Charles Darwin, if not actually the author of our imaginary play, is at least entitled to credit for inspiring the theme. Of course, it is unlikely that he had in mind as primitive a conflict for existence as this when he formulated his principles of evolution, but there is no reason why his doctrine of "survival of the fittest" would not have applied to our primeval cast of characters. In fact, as we have seen, nothing could have prevented it. The principles involved are exactly the same as those underlying any number of physical and chemical phenomena in which parallel processes of different and self-aggrandizing rates of activity simultaneously have access to the same source of supply of basic ingredients. "Evolution" may be widely considered to be a law of biology but, like all other biological principles we have encountered, its roots are firmly implanted in the ordinary laws of physics.

The ultimate result of the interspecies struggle for existence among the primordial coacervates had to be the same as the ultimate result of all evolutionary competitions—the suppression of the poorly adapted and the proliferation of the well adapted. The seas must have come to abound in droplets containing a mixture of catalysts and other ingredients that supported a variety of internal chemical activities which not only made rapid and effective use of the raw materials then available in the waters of the earth but also maintained an internal organization and membrane properties that contributed to balanced growth and reproduction. However, despite our imaginary dramatic production, it is not necessary to conclude that only one species finally survived. Differences in climate and local chemical conditions among different regions of the seas would result in different relative survival values for the competing species and would lead to strong geographical influences on the nature of the local population. Changes in the chemistry of the sea resulting from gradual changes in the earth's atmosphere and surface composition would also have preserved a larger number of species than could otherwise have coexisted by preventing the evolutionary processes from going to completion and becoming static.

In any event, the principles of evolution would not have led to a static situation, even if the environmental conditions of the coacervates had been uniform and unchanging. For the perpetual random jostling of the organic and inorganic constituents inside the coacervates would frequently result in the formation of new types of molecules. Perhaps one of these molecules out of a million would help catalyze some new chain of reactions within the coacervate. And, in one of a million of these new reaction chains, one of the products might be the newly invented molecule. If so, autocatalysis could occur, the new molecular form could become abundant, and the associated set of chemical reactions it facilitated could become part of the standard metabolism of succeeding generations of coacervates. To be sure, in our hypothethical example this would occur only once for every million million random formations of new molecular types, but this would be more than often enough to provide for the coacervates a dynamic pattern of evolutionary development. The time between successive events at the molecular level is so few millionths of a second and the time available is so many millions of years that the raw material of evolutionary change can easily consist of such seemingly unlikely accidental molecular juxtapositions or rearrangements. In fact, because of the "trying out" of new combinations that must occur ceaselessly in any substance that is not held at the absolute zero of temperature, we can be sure that sooner or later pure chance will lead to the formation of *any* arrangement of the available materials that the laws of physics and chemistry will permit to hold together. Thus, new and improved molecular types, with their associated autocatalytic chains of chemical reactions, would have been continually "sought out" and incorporated into the architecture and metabolism of the coacervates to improve their growth and reproduction characteristics.

The cumulative results of these natural-selection processes would ultimately have included the appearance of other new structural and metabolic features. For example, occasionally a chain reaction that got started would have produced, among other things, substances that tended to coagulate and thus form solid inclusions or membranes within the coacervate. Because of physical adhesive forces, these new inclusions would have trapped and bound, in an extended two-dimensional configuration, some of the molecules floating in the surrounding fluid. In some instances, the surface-bound configuration of the trapped molecules would have had a higher chemical reactivity than the unbound configuration, thereby increasing the growth rate of the coacervate. Ultimately, therefore, evolutionary selection would have made commonplace coacervates with composition leading to included membranes.

Another likely early aberration in coacervate structure would have been the formation of droplets within droplets. It will be recalled that organic materials in the primeval pools spontaneously coalesced into spherical droplets because of strong attractive forces between their molecules and that this was followed by the development of more or less permanent enclosing membranes. In the same way, certain products of the coacervate metabolism could coalesce into "inclusions" separated from the bulk of the coacervate fluids by enclosing membranes of their own.* The differential permeability of the membranes would block the transmission of certain molecules while allowing others to interpenetrate freely. This would result in the concentration of certain substances within the inclusions and different ones outside. Different series of reactions could then occur in the two regions of the coacervate. Among the countless millions of times that such inclusions spontaneously formed within billions of coacervates, there would occasionally be a combination having above-average survival value. The special conditions preserved in the semi-isolated inclusion would support chemical reactions having a certain product that would not only be able to penetrate the enclosing membrane but, once on the outside, would be unusually effective in accelerating the external pattern of chemical reactions. These reactions, in the surrounding "body" of the coacervate, would then have as one product a substance that could enter the inclusion and further stimulate its synthesizing processes. Such a mutually facilitating interaction would contribute above-average growth characteristics to the complex coacervate, with the inevitable ultimate evolutionary popularizing among the coacervate population of an inclusion/body structure and associated chemistry that started out as a rare and improbable combination.

---

* "Inclusion" is used here in a general sense. Modern descendants of such coacervate structures would probably include not only the nuclei common to the cells of most organisms but also the smaller anatomic "organelles" that are found in the more primitive bacteria as well as in the cells of more advanced organisms.

Even time-varying metabolic processes would be expected to result from the operation of the physical principles of evolution. Consider, for example, a complex coacervate similar to that just described but in which the ingredients that accelerate the growth reactions are not catalysts but instead get "used up" in the reactions they promote. Suppose further that the body reaction must go on for a substantial period of time before the production of the ingredient that then migrates to the inclusion to participate in its internal chemistry and that the resulting reaction in the inclusion also requires a substantial period before it can generate and send the other accelerating ingredient back to the body. This is a "positive-feedback system" with time lags. Such a system, familiar to electronic engineers, results in oscillatory behavior. In such a coacervate, in both body and inclusions, the chemical conditions would change periodically. In sophisticated coacervates, comparatively high on the evolutionary scale, the cyclic process would probably not be so simple as merely a successive acceleration and deceleration of a single chain of chemical reactions in body and inclusions. Instead, in addition to the "main chain" of chemistry involved in the cyclic process, there could be "side chains" of secondary reactions with various products, possibly including some useful for the main reaction chain. For example, the periodic exhaustion of the special inclusion-originating ingredient needed in the body of the coacervate could permit new reactions that would not be possible in the presence of that special ingredient. These other reactions might produce a substance needed in some subsequent step of the coacervate chemistry. Thus, temporal cycling of the coacervate chemical activity could have survival value and gradually become "standard equipment" in successive generations of coacervates.

Such evolutionary processes would have resulted in a gradual but inexorable speeding up of the rate of development of new species of lifelike structures. As natural selection brought to prominence forms of organization of matter characterized by greater and greater efficiency in the use of the raw materials of the seas, the increasing rates of growth and reproduction of these new forms finally must have compressed into centuries a degree of evolutionary development that had previously required hundreds of millenniums. If the first billion years of the earth's history was required for the tortuous development of a handful of coacervate droplets rugged enough to leave their pools of incubation and survive in the open seas, the second billion years must have witnessed increases in chemical and structural sophistication that were fantastic, compared with the accomplishments of the earlier era.

Earlier, in our recognition of the lifelike characteristics of the primitive coacervates, we had to ask ourselves whether our discussion had carried us over the line dividing the realm of inanimate mechanism from that of animate organism. As we now contemplate the tremendous increase of sophistication that the natural forces of evolution must have brought to the chemistry and structure of the coacervates, the question becomes even more insistent. In fact, from this point on, we should find it awkward if we could not start employing more of the language of biology in discussing the aggregations of matter we must deal with. We must soon start talking about "single-celled organisms" rather than coacervate droplets.

But if the property of "life" has really attached itself to our curious bags of chemicals, this would appear to be a development that no author should allow to slip unheeded into his text. After all, in such a book as this one, there can be no accomplishment more significant than establishing that the prosaic operation of the ordinary laws of physics on the materials and in the environment of the primordial earth ultimately leads to the appearance of living organisms. It would appear that the author would have the responsibility of calling the reader's attention to the point at which the transition from nonlife to life occurs, so that due notice could be taken of this most important development.

The trouble is that no one has designed a definition of life that permits clear-cut distinction between living and nonliving forms of matter. Most would say that a single-celled amoeba is alive and that a primeval pool of hot dilute soup is not. In terms of the organization of this book, there would probably be general agreement that the subject matter of a couple of chapters back was inanimate and that the subject matter a couple of chapters farther on is animate. However, there would be little agreement on precisely where the line between nonlife and life is crossed. This makes it difficult for an author to achieve the dramatic effect to which he feels an event of such importance entitles him. His defense must be that the colorlessness of the treatment is a consequence of the peculiarity of the subject matter rather than of his own literary inadequacy.

Let us therefore take up again the thread of our narrative. We shall do so by exploring the continuing evolutionary development of what we shall now call the single-celled organisms of the late primeval world. As we encounter more evidence of the almost explosive accelerating power of the forces of evolution, we shall, of course, keep constantly in mind the fact that nothing vitalistic or even uniquely "biological" is involved. The appearance of effective evolutionary processes awaited only the development of the competitive conditions fundamental to the operation of the principle of natural selection. When those conditions appeared, so did evolution.

The basic rules of the game we are playing are still the laws of physics.

part 3

A Great Leap Forward:
Development of
the Nucleic Acid / Enzyme Mechanisms

chapter 9

A Major Evolutionary Discovery: The Nucleic Acids

We are now ready to attempt to bridge the gap between primordial coacervates and modern single-celled organisms. Superficially, the gap might appear to be a narrow one. After all, we have traced the development of our primitive bags of chemicals to forms so advanced as to include parallel chains of chemical reactions involving numerous molecular types, partial isolation of different regions by membrane-enclosed inclusions, and even time-varying metabolism resulting from the interaction of two or more chemical subsystems of the coacervates. Nevertheless, cell-like though these properties appear to be, it would be a mistake to underestimate the great differences that separate modern organisms from even the most advanced type of coacervate that our discussion to this point has permitted us to visualize. Biological research in recent years has revealed the existence of remarkably complex mechanisms in even the simplest of single-celled creatures. We shall yet have need of a combination of imagination and confidence in the power of evolution if we are to convince ourselves of the essential kinship between the curious chemical structures we have been considering and the modern organisms we hope to bring under our purview.

Although much of the complexity in structure and function of modern single-celled organisms can be generally understood as the result of detailed progressive refinement under the control of the natural-selection processes already discussed, there exists in all life forms today a basic set of mechanisms that has not yet appeared in our discussion of the development of coacervates. These mechanisms, in substantially the same form, control the growth and reproduction of viruses, bacteria, plants, and animals. Nucleic acid is the key ingredient in the modern control process. One of the fastest-moving and most exciting fields of current scientific research is that of *molecular genetics,* which deals with the way that giant molecules of *ribonucleic acid* (RNA) or *deoxyribonucleic acid* (DNA) exert precise architectural control over the growth of living forms, determining whether the outcome is to be amoeba or man. Thus, if our thesis as to the evolution of life from nonlife is to carry conviction, we must show that there is a plausible way in which the operation of the ordinary laws of physics could have resulted in the "discovery" and incorporation of the powerful nucleic acid genetic-control mechanisms in modern organisms. This task will occupy our attention for the next several chapters.

But before we undertake our difficult new assignment, some comment on the logical structure of the ensuing development would appear to be in order. First of all, a word of reassurance to those readers who are not familiar with recent developments in molecular genetics: no background in the subject will be as-

sumed in the following treatment. On the contrary, the procedure will be to show how the simple principles of chemical
evolution we have been considering might have operated to produce certain types of molecules possessing interesting new
characteristics and how, with further natural selection, these
characteristics might have come to be exploited in the control of
growth and reproduction. Thus we shall attempt to *derive* molecular genetics from basic evolutionary principles. In the process,
many of the interesting known features of the hereditary mechanisms will appear as consequences of the development.

But the fact that the conclusions will coincide nicely with what
is known about molecular genetics must not be interpreted by the
reader as implying scientific rigor in the intervening argument.
For no one today, least of all the author, knows enough about the
almost limitless chemical alternatives available to developing organisms to plot anything like a certain evolutionary path span-
ning the billions of years separating primordial coacervates from
modern living forms. And there are no fossil records to indicate
which was the actual path by which modern organisms came by
their present properties. The gaps are so great and the steps so
numerous that it seems unlikely we shall ever know for sure just
how we got from there to here.

Therefore, the ensuing "derivation" of some of the principles
of modern molecular genetics from the workings of evolution on
the primordial coacervates must be taken for what it is—a work
of fiction. To be sure, the evolutionary episodes of which it is
composed have been postulated because they lead to consequences that are compatible with modern knowledge. Nevertheless, the story told is almost certainly not "true" in any detailed
sense. The best that can be hoped for is that it is "true to life" in
that the events that it portrays are similar enough in quality to
those which actually transpired as to lead to generally valid con-

clusions about the nature, although not necessarily the details, of the prehistory of biology.

With the limitations of the treatment clearly understood in advance, let us now undertake the assignment of tracing a possible evolutionary path of development of the mechanisms, based on nucleic acid molecules, by means of which growth and reproduction are controlled in all modern living organisms.

chapter 10

The Generation and Reproduction of Nucleic Acid Molecules

In anticipation of the eventual necessity for a serious study of nucleic acids, occasional references to them and to their properties have been made in earlier chapters. We have learned that nucleic acids, like proteins, form long-chain molecules. However, unlike proteins, nucleic acids do not have 6-atom arrangements of carbon, hydrogen, oxygen, and nitrogen as their basic structural segments. Instead, each "vertebra" of the backbone of the nucleic acid molecule consists of a configuration, called a *sugar phosphate,* containing 5 carbon atoms, 8 hydrogen atoms, 5 or 6 oxygens, and 1 phosphorus, bound together by mutual electric forces in a standardized spatial arrangement.* The overall distribution

---

* There are actually two slightly different forms of nucleic acid. The one with 6 oxygen atoms in each vertebral segment is called ribonucleic acid (RNA); that with only 5 oxygen atoms is known as deoxyribonucleic acid (DNA). In modern organisms, as we shall see later, the two kinds of

of electric charge is such that one end of a sugar phosphate attaches relatively easily to a particular corner of another sugar phosphate, thereby leading to the formation of the observed long chains.

In our study of protein molecules in Chapter 4 we saw that chemical individuality was conferred on the otherwise identical segments of the chain by the attachment, to each segment, of one of 20 different side chains of atomic configurations. The backbone segment with attached side chain was called an amino acid, and the remarkable variety of protein substances was found to be a consequence of the number of different molecules that could be built by hooking together long sequences of the 20 different kinds of amino acids.

Nucleic acids employ a similar arrangement of attached side chains to confer individuality on the segments of the long molecules. However, only 4 types of side chain appear in a molecule of RNA or DNA, instead of the 20 that appear in protein molecules. The nucleic acid side chains contain only carbon, hydrogen, oxygen, and nitrogen and involve, in each case, a characteristic configuration of 12 to 16 atoms. Although the combination of the sugar phosphate backbone segment with its side chain possesses acid properties, there is no such common chemical property as the ammonia-releasing characteristic that led to the generic term *amino acid* to designate the structural units of protein molecules. The corresponding term for the nucleic acid molecular structural unit is *nucleotide.* To be sure, the names *adenine, guanine, cytosine,* and *uracil* that are given to the four different side chains of RNA lead to *adenylic acid, guanylic acid, cytidilic acid,* and *uridylic acid* as designations of the individual types of

---

nucleic acid have developed specialties, being separately responsible for different features of the genetic processes. However, in the primitive era under discussion, it is simplest to consider RNA and DNA to be equivalent in their functions.

nucleotide, but we shall have little need for such terminology.* We should, however, note that the term *base* is commonly used instead of "side chain" in technical discussions of the nucleic acids.

One of the most important similarities between nucleic acids and proteins is their common likelihood of formation under the conditions that prevailed when the earth was young. In the experiments considered in Chapter 5, wherein the hypothesized primordial atmosphere was exposed to ultraviolet radiation, radioactive bombardment, heat, and electric discharge, the amino acids needed for protein formation were generated, to be sure. But in addition, the sugars, phosphates, and bases that appear in nucleic acids were sometimes produced. And the local conditions on the infant earth that occasionally caused amino acid segments to hook together to form simple precursors of modern proteins must sometimes also have produced primitive forms of nucleic acid molecules.

Let us therefore suppose that a primitive molecule of nucleic acid has formed in this way and that it consists of a string of nucleotides of the different types A, G, C, and U (the letters representing the distinctive side chains, or bases: adenine, guanine, cytosine, and uracil).† Suppose, further, that this molecule happens to be immersed in a fluid containing an abundance of the ingredients from which other nucleic acid molecules might be constructed—including nucleotides of the four significant types. Under these circumstances interesting chemical reactions may occur. To start with, the free nucleotides floating around in the mixture will tend to stick to the outer, unattached ends of the

* In DNA the side chain *uracil* is replaced by *thymine,* which differs from uracil only in having an aggregation of 1 carbon and 2 hydrogen atoms tacked on to one out-of-the-way corner.

† Or A, G, C, and T, if the molecule happens to be of the DNA, rather than the RNA, variety.

bases that project from the backbone of the nucleic acid molecule. This by itself is not surprising; probably many different kinds of molecular fragments have patterns of electric charge permitting some kind of partial fit with the patterns of charge at the free ends of the nucleic acid bases; under the ceaseless jostling of thermal agitation, temporary attachments of many varieties must be continually made and broken. However, it happens that certain of the attachments that can be made between the free and the bound nucleotides possess unusual characteristics. This is true of the attachment of a free U nucleotide * to a bound A nucleotide (or vice versa) and of the attachment of a free C nucleotide to a bound G nucleotide (or vice versa). The first important characteristic of an A-U * or a C-G combination is the strength of the attachment; in either case the interposition of hydrogen atoms between oxygen and nitrogen atoms produces a relatively tight bond. The second important characteristic of these two combinations is that both result in approximately the same length of structure when measured at right angles to the backbone of the supporting nucleic acid molecule. The A and G bases are long; the C and U * bases are short; the A-U * and C-G combinations are of about the same length.

What difference does all this make? Just this: the relatively strong binding forces that cause A-U * and C-G combinations to be more lasting than others also line up the free ends of the newly attached nucleotides (the ends farthest from the backbone of the original nucleic acid molecule) in just the right positions to permit them to be easily hooked together. The result is a new nucleic acid molecule, complete with backbone and side chains, attached in Siamese-twin fashion to the original molecule. The resulting double molecule is in effect a ladder; the two uprights consist of the sugar-phosphate backbones, and the uniform-

* Substitute T for U, in DNA.

Fig. 10-1. Double molecule of nucleic acid (RNA), showing sugar-phosphate backbones and conjugated bases (original single molecule on left, stippled).

length crossbars consist of the A-U,* U-A,* C-G, and G-C base pairings of the two molecules (Fig. 10-1).

Since the reader has been warned that this treatment is rife with speculation, it is therefore probably worthwhile to point out that what has been discussed up to this point rests on a firm experimental basis. In 1953 J. D. Watson and F. H. C. Crick,

* Substitute T for U, in DNA.

working at Cambridge University with X-ray diffraction photographs of nucleic acids (DNA) made by the English physicist M. H. F. Wilkins and his colleague Rosalind Franklin, succeeded in establishing the main features of the modern theory of nucleic acid structure. (For this work the three scientists were awarded a Nobel Prize in 1962.) Watson and Crick were able to show that the kind of ladderlike structure just described actually does occur and that the rungs of the ladder always consist of the long-short combinations of bases. In fact, it was later discovered that these ladderlike molecules of nucleic acid can even be formed from single-stranded molecules in the test tube, in the complete absence of living cells, provided that a "broth" containing the necessary ingredients is supplied. In the laboratory situation this broth must include more than the original single-stranded molecules and the four kinds of nucleotides to be incorporated in the new nucleic acid; it must also contain catalysts to speed up the reaction and energy-rich molecules to provide the motive power needed to "zip" the chains together by temporarily attaching themselves to the segmental components. As we have earlier observed, such additional ingredients usually facilitate the reactions in living organisms also.

A slight complication should be mentioned at this point, lest the reader fail to recognize, in the ladderlike structure described here, the "double-stranded" nucleic acid molecule that forms the subject of so much discussion these days. For a commonly mentioned feature of double-stranded nucleic acid (also established by Watson and Crick) is the helical form of its molecule. It is as though the uprights of the ladder we have been discussing were flexible and the top and bottom ends of the ladder had been grasped and twisted in opposite directions until a form of double corkscrew resulted. X-ray photographs leave no doubt that such a double helix is the normal configuration of a free double-stranded molecule of nucleic acid. However, this geometrical complication is of little apparent significance in most of the processes we have to consider, and it will therefore be ignored when the resulting task of description is made easier thereby.

Now let us see what can happen to our ladderlike double-stranded molecule of nucleic acid. One interesting possibility is that it will separate into two single-stranded molecules of nucleic acid. This can happen because the so-called hydrogen bonds that tie together the A-U * and C-G bases at their points of contact in each rung of the ladder, though stronger than other bonds that sometimes cause temporary linking of molecular fragments, are still comparatively weak and can be broken without disrupting the rest of the structure. In the test tube, the addition of acid or alkali to the surrounding fluid or gentle heating to just under the boiling point of water will do the trick; in modern organisms, the presence of certain organic catalysts will cause the hydrogen bonds to break at ordinary temperatures. In either case, the result is as though each rung of the ladder had been sawed in two at the junction of the conjugated bases. This yields two separate single-stranded nucleic acid molecules in place of the double-stranded one (Fig. 10-2). One of these single-stranded molecules is just the original piece of nucleic acid with which our discussion started several pages back. The other is a new molecule, different from the original one, but different in an orderly way. It is a "complement" of the original in the sense that the sequence of bases, or side chains, along its backbone is specified by substituting a U base * for every A base of the original molecule, a G †️ for every C, a C for every G, and an A for every U.†️

We are finally about to discover a clue to the mystery of the great importance of nucleic acid in life processes. For consider what will happen if the pair of reactions we have been discussing

---

* Substitute T for U, in DNA.

†️ This is for RNA; a T base, in the case of DNA.

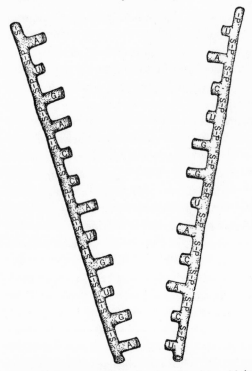

Fig. 10-2. Two single molecules of nucleic acid (RNA), resulting from breaking of hydrogen bonds between conjugated bases of double molecule (original single molecule on left, stippled).

is repeated, employing as starting material *both* the original molecule and its complement. This time each of the two single-stranded molecules will form a complement, and the complement of the molecule which itself was the complement of the original molecule will be a carbon copy of the original! Here is indeed a new and interesting phenomenon—a long-chain organic molecule that controls a cycle of chemical reactions so as to produce exact duplicates of itself.

To be sure, we have had to postulate a cyclically varying environment for our reacting ingredients. At times the fluids surrounding the nucleic acid molecules have had to contain the nucleotides, energy-rich molecules and catalysts needed to support the formation of double-stranded structures; at other times they have had to be different at least to the extent of containing hydrogen-bond-destroying ingredients that break double-stranded molecules in two. In the era of the early coacervates it seems most unlikely that such a cyclical change in chemical environment could have been provided by the simple structure and metabolism that must have then prevailed. However, with the evolutionary development of increasing chemical and architectural sophistication discussed in Chapter 8, a time must ultimately have come when the required cyclically varying conditions could have been sustained. The conditions postulated would still have been unlikely but probably not so unlikely that they would not have occurred from time to time during the many millions of years at the disposal of the remarkably prolific species-generating processes of evolution.

Note that we have as yet discovered nothing about the nucleic acid molecules to suggest that a mechanism for their production would have any kind of survival value for the host coacervate, interesting though we have judged such a mechanism to be. We are therefore, to this point, discussing a by-product of the coacervate metabolism. We are, in effect, assuming that the relatively complex metabolic processes that sustained the growth and reproduction of certain advanced coacervate species just happened to include chemical reactions that from time to time produced the special materials, such as catalysts and energizing substances, needed for the two-stage synthesis of nucleic acids. Under such circumstances we are observing that nucleic acid molecules would in fact have been produced, whether or not they were useful to the host coacervate.

Of course, to account for the fact that organisms containing nucleic acid ultimately starved out all others and are the only forms of life that persist today, we have to find some way in which nucleic acid could have become involved in the chemistry underlying growth and reproduction so as to contribute survivability advantages to the host coacervates. To attain such a goal, which we may hope to do in the next chapter, we are going to have to invoke certain properties of nucleic acid that arise directly from the sheer physical length of its molecules. Therefore, before terminating the present discussion of the nucleic acid generation and reproduction mechanisms, we must show that the processes we have postulated are capable of leading to the formation of long and complex molecules, and not just short molecules consisting of only a few segments.

To this end we should first note that the two-stage process described so far is strictly a copying process—it could not originate new kinds of molecules.* To get the process started, we had to assume that a molecule or molecules of nucleic acid were somehow "provided"; after that, additional copies of the starting molecules would be manufactured at a significant rate. The starting molecules, in the original coacervates embodying the process, would have had to be more or less spontaneously generated when nucleotides happened to bump together in just the proper way. We know that the raw materials needed were continually formed in the primordial atmosphere, and experimental evidence suggests that the automatic hooking together of the constituents would have occurred from time to time. However, such random collisions would have been vastly more effective in producing simple molecules than complex ones. The greater the number of segments in a "long-chain" molecule manufactured in this random fashion, the rarer would the molecule be in the population

---

* Except, of course, for the complementary forms of the originally supplied nucleic acid molecules.

of organic ingredients inhabiting the primeval seas. To keep our present story believable, therefore, we must assume that the molecules produced in the earliest forms of nucleic-acid-synthesizing coacervates were short and simple and thus, in terms of our upcoming genetic requirements, not very interesting.

Happily, there is a way of getting around this difficulty. Organic catalysts are known today that, in the test tube, enormously accelerate the linking of nucleotides into nucleic acid molecules. Under the influence of such catalysts, chains of one thousand or more nucleotides have been formed in the laboratory. To be sure, it is most unlikely that catalysts of the late coacervate period had anything like the complex and sophisticated structure of today's product. On the other hand, the modern reactions go to completion in seconds. A primitive ancestor of modern organic catalysts could have been of great evolutionary significance even though it required years instead of seconds to achieve its catalytic results. The rules of the game of speculation we are playing would appear to permit us to postulate the existence of such catalysts in the era in question.

Specifically, let us assume that some of the coacervates (not necessarily those which featured the nucleic acid reproduction mechanism) developed chemical reaction patterns that produced, as by-products, substances that were able to catalyze the attachment of additional nucleotides to the ends of nucleic acid molecules. The ultimate bursting apart of the parent coacervates would then spill into the seas some of these catalytic molecules, which from time to time would be accidentally incorporated in other coacervates. In particular, let us consider the consequences if some of these catalytic molecules happened to enter individual members of a species of coacervate possessing the nucleic acid reproduction mechanism we have been discussing. In evolutionary terms the results of such an accident could be profound. These new catalysts, even though present in the coacervates in only minute quantities, would occasionally add nucleotides on to some of the nucleic acid molecules under continual production by the co-acervate metabolism. Because of the independence of the copying mechanism on the length or specific base sequence of the nucleic acid, the new and longer molecule would then go into production and soon become abundant. Occasionally one of these longer molecules would in turn be lengthened by the action of the catalyst; this would result in the appearance of substantial numbers of a still more complex nucleic acid molecule, and so on. In this way, coacervate individuals blessed with a combination of the nucleic acid reproduction mechanism and a few nucleotide-linking catalytic molecules would automatically and continually develop an increasing variety of nucleic acid products. The ultimate result would be a population of nucleic acid molecules in the seas that would grow steadily not only in numbers but also in average complexity. The molecules containing thousands of nucleotides that are commonplace in modern organisms could well owe their complexity—and therefore, as we shall see later, their remarkable ability to regulate and control life processes—to such a past developmental history.

Thus we have finally been able to rationalize the appearance of advanced forms of coacervates containing quantities of long-chain nucleic acid molecules together with mechanisms for their precise reproduction. We are clearly moving toward a hypothesis to account for the remarkable monopoly of control of the growth and reproduction processes that is exhibited by the nucleic acid mechanisms of modern organisms. As our next step, let us see whether we can discover any properties of the new and complex nucleic acid molecules that might have bestowed increased survivability on their coacervate hosts.

BIBLIOGRAPHY

Asimov, I., *The Genetic Code* (The Orion Press, Inc., New York, 1962), chap. 7, "The Cinderella Compound," chap. 8, "From Chain to Helix," and chap. 9, "The Cooperating Strands."

Beadle, G. W., "The New Genetics," in 1964 *Britannica Book of the Year* (Encyclopaedia Britannica, Inc., Chicago, 1964), pp. 45–72.

Herskowitz, I. H., *Genetics* (Little, Brown and Company, Boston, 1962), chap. 34, "Organization, Replication, and Types of DNA *in Vivo*."

chapter 11

The Development
of Architectural Talents
by the Nucleic Acids

We must now try to imagine what the nucleic acid molecules, in the late coacervate/early cellular * era, could have done besides reproduce their own kind. For definiteness, let us consider a coacervate or cell containing large numbers of nucleic acid molecules of different compositions and lengths. Let us assume, moreover, that much of the nucleic acid is in its single-stranded form at the time we commence our observations. This could be because not enough time has yet elapsed for the growth of the Siamese-twin configurations since the cyclically changing chemistry of the cell last produced the conditions that split the double molecules into single ones. In any event, let us follow the adven-

---

* In this chapter we shall deliberately slip into cellular terminology.

109

tures of a single-stranded nucleic acid molecule as it floats around in the cellular fluid.

We know, of course, that the floating around of such a molecule would not be a completely passive performance. We have already dealt with the tendency, arising from the electric fields associated with atoms and molecules, for some of the small organic and inorganic molecular fragments that inhabit the cellular fluid to attach themselves to local regions of the nucleic acid molecules. In the preceding chapter we concentrated on one type of such attachment process—that which causes a single molecule of nucleic acid to grow into a double one by conjugation of its bases. At that time we did not concern ourselves greatly with competition from other kinds of attaching molecular fragments, although we knew that such other attachments were bound to occur from time to time. Our lack of concern for such competition was based on our awareness that most of these other attachments would be tenuous and quickly broken, since the randomly encountered molecular fragments would usually not "mate" very well with the nearby parts of the nucleic acid. Our discussion implied that, upon the approach of a free nucleotide to a suitable region of a molecule of nucleic acid, the strong binding forces that would come into play would result in the displacement of any lightly held "impurity" in favor of the attachment of the arriving nucleotide.

Such a tendency for loosely held fragments to be displaced by molecules of greater binding energy is probably adequate to render inconsequential the large majority of the nucleic acid molecule's casual encounters in the cellular fluid. Nevertheless, there would appear to be possibilities for attachments of kinds that would not necessarily yield to such displacement forces. For example, two different nucleic acid molecules would occasionally bump together. And once in a while such a collision might bring together short regions of the two long molecules carrying base sequences complementary to one another—an A base opposed to a U* base, then a G opposed to a C, and so on. The resulting multiple attachment could constitute a much stronger connection than that resulting from the usual casual encounter between molecules of different types.

To be sure, collisions between nucleic acid molecules would be rare, unless the concentration of nucleic acid in the cellular fluid were exceedingly high. There is a related kind of encounter, however, that would occur much more frequently—the collision of one part of a long nucleic acid molecule with another part of the same molecule. For the nucleic acid backbone is supple; it can turn back upon itself like a rope. Under the ceaseless churning that thermal agitation imposes on the molecules of any fluid, each long chain of nucleic acid would be continually bending and twisting, frequently thereby bringing normally remote parts of itself into temporary contact. An occasional attachment would be of just the nature described in the example of the encounter of two different nucleic acid molecules. If not an unusually strong attachment (that is, involving a considerable number of conjugated bases), it would soon be broken under the stress of random thermal agitation. However, if a special way of folding the long molecule back upon itself *could* result in a binding together of the two halves strong enough to survive, it would eventually be "found"; the random processes would ultimately make nearly the right kind of fold, the resulting attractive forces would do the rest, and the long molecule would lock together in a characteristic folded configuration.

Of course, certain conditions would have to be met by a single-stranded nucleic acid molecule before it could be eligible to form a folded configuration. In particular, a certain minimum length would have to be exceeded in order that the two halves of the

* Substitute T for U, in DNA.

folded molecule could make enough mutual bonds to provide the needed attachment strength. X-ray analysis of the nucleic acid in modern organisms shows that such folded structures, which are abundant in all cells, usually involve seventy to eighty nucleotides. A combination of speculation and evidence suggests that there may be nothing very critical about the specific sequence of bases along the backbone of a successfully folded molecule. Figure 11-1 shows how a molecule of random base sequence might be able to form a folded or hairpin structure involving complementary pairing of most of its bases by the simple expedient of pushing away from the primary folded structure an occasional nucleotide segment that does not fit the base pattern of the opposite arm of the structure. X-ray measurements strongly suggest that this kind of expedient distortion of the hairpin does actually occur and that the schematic drawing of Figure 11-1 is probably fairly realistic.*

* Folded configurations would not be assumed by all nucleic acid molecules even if their length and base sequence were favorable. For the reproduction process would sometimes prevent the formation of folded molecules; to the extent to which the projecting bases had already been mated with conjugate nucleotides from the surrounding fluid, there would be a decrease in the probability that the different parts of the flailing molecule would stick together. However, it is not hard to postulate conditions that would cause the competition to be frequently resolved in favor of the formation of folded configurations rather than double molecules. For one thing, as mentioned in the preceding chapter, catalysts and energy-supplying molecules must be available in the cellular fluid if the formation of double molecules is to proceed at a significant rate. The chore for which these molecular aids are required does not have to do with the conjugation of the nucleotide bases; this goes easily. Rather, the additional energy and catalytic assist are needed to connect the sugar phosphate ends of the nucleotides. But this requirement does not exist for the formation of a folded configuration of a single molecule. Therefore, we might well expect the folding process to occur more rapidly than the reproduction process for

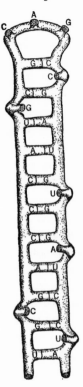

Fig. 11-1. A possible "folded" arrangement for a nucleic acid (RNA) molecule. (The bending of the backbone to accommodate the extraneous nucleotides would be considerably less abrupt, in the actual twisted three-dimensional situation, than this flat schematic drawing suggests.)

the molecules in question. This would be particularly true if, as we can easily postulate, the supply of catalysts and energy-contributing molecules were low in the vicinity of some of the single-stranded nucleic acid. Under such circumstances we can easily imagine that the occasional free nucleotide that attached itself to conjugate bases along the backbone of the nu-

To be sure, the actual configuration of the folded molecule would not look much like the two-dimensional pattern of Figure 11-1. The same electric forces that cause double-stranded nucleic acid molecules to form a double helix would operate to impose a twist on the folded molecule. The imperfections caused by the nonmatching bases would probably also distort the helix, and the final result would be a three-dimensional configuration with a pattern of atomic arrangement and external electric fields that, in the last analysis, would be completely determined by the specific sequence of bases along the backbone of the original unfolded nucleic acid molecule.

Such a hairpin-folded, imperfectly helically-twisted molecule would possess some special properties arising out of its specific three-dimensional pattern of electric charge. In particular, it would be likely to have an affinity for certain kinds of molecular fragments. For example, a particular sequence of nucleotides might result in such a pattern of hairpin folding and partial helical twisting as to produce, in some portion of the molecule, a very good fit for a sugar fragment. Another molecule with a different sequence of nucleotides might include within its three-dimensional contours a good "mold" for holding a particular kind of amino acid, and so on. Assuming the existence of such ingredients in the surrounding fluid, continued floating around of the nucleic acid molecules would ultimately result in getting most of them coupled to whatever specific kinds of molecular fragments their own special patterns of electric fields best equip them to carry.

But the automatic formation of a folded and twisted structure

cleic acid molecule would be displaced by the stronger binding forces brought into play by the tendency toward multiple affiliation of the components of the two arms of the molecule itself.

clutching in its tentacles an attractive fragment of molecular flotsam is not the only nonreproductive fate that can befall a nucleic acid molecule in the cellular fluid. Modern evidence shows that longer varieties of these molecules can become tightly bound to the surfaces of solid particles. The particles on which such attachment occurs are today called *microsomes,* and they are a conspicuous feature of all modern cells. We have no difficulty in rationalizing the evolutionary origin of such inclusions; the precipitation of some of the chemical by-products of metabolism would doubtless have produced solid particles in some of the early coacervates. The requirement of length in the surface-bound nucleic acid molecules (in modern organisms each contains about 1,500 nucleotides, although, of course, it is unlikely that the primitive forms were of this degree of complexity) is probably generally understandable in terms of the ever-present competition between combining and disrupting forces. Unless the molecule is long enough to provide many local points of attachment to the supporting surface, the ceaseless jostling to which it is subjected by the random thermal agitation of the surrounding molecules will jar it loose. Perhaps for a similar reason, a successfully surface-bound nucleic acid molecule appears to be fully extended, rather than folded back upon itself. Further, the long molecule is held to the surface in such a way as not to neutralize the pattern of electric fields that results from the specific sequence of bases along the backbone. It is as though, on encountering a solid surface, the nucleic acid molecule were to lie down on its back, extending its A, C, G, and U* side chains into the surrounding fluid (Fig. 11-2). For the bound molecules are chemically reactive. In particular, they can make attachments to other nucleic acid components by conjugation of complementary bases,

---

* Substitute T for U, in DNA.

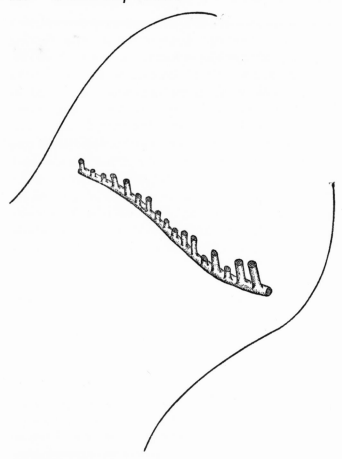

Fig. 11-2. Attachment of a long molecule of nucleic acid to a microsomal surface.

as we saw could occur upon the accidental encounter of two float-ing nucleic acid molecules.*

---

* This does not have to mean, however, that the long surface-bound molecule of nucleic acid would rapidly accrue to itself conjugate nucleotides and bind them together to form a double molecule. In fact, the story we

Now we are confronted with a most interesting situation; for a folded and twisted "floating" nucleic acid molecule of the kind we discussed earlier will tend to stick to a stretched-out, surface-held molecule if it happens to approach the right part of the stretched-out molecule in just the right way. Such an affinity arises because the floating molecule has one or more "sticky" points occurring at places along the folded structure where there is a sequence of several unpaired bases. At the hairpin turn there must always be such a sequence of greater or lesser length depending upon the flexibility of the backbone—that is, on how sharply it can bend before the restoring forces set up by the distortion of the molecular structure become too large. These restoring forces would also naturally result in a rotation of the nonconjugated side chains around the backbone and out of the plane of the hairpin (Fig. 11-1), thereby rendering the sequence of bases involved more freely available for coupling to another molecule. The result would be this: If the folded molecule, under the influence of random thermal motion, should bring its hairpin-curved terminus close to a surface-bound nucleic acid molecule at a place along its backbone where the sequence of several bases happened to be complementary to the sequence of bases along the hairpin curve, the attractive forces resulting from the base complementarity would pull the folded molecule into position and it would

---

are inventing requires that this should happen rarely, if at all. It is not hard to imagine conditions that would hold such double-molecule formation to a low level. For example, the catalyst that zips together the sugar phosphate ends of the conjugated nucleotides to tie up the backbone structure of the Siamese-twin molecule may not be able to operate effectively when the generating single molecule is stretched out on a solid surface. Alternatively, a low concentration of the catalytic ingredients in the vicinity of the solid inclusions could so slow the rate of double-molecule generation as to permit the occasional conjugated nucleotide of the forming molecule to be easily displaced by the stronger binding forces of the molecular attachments we are about to consider.

stick to the surface-bound molecule. On a long surface-bound molecule there would, on the average, be a number of places where the sequence would be complementary to that of the unpaired bases of a particular type of floating molecule; molecules of this type would tend to be found attached to such places. Other places along the backbone of the surface-bound molecule would be the natural resting points for folded and twisted floating molecules of different nucleic acid types with different sequences of unpaired bases featuring their hairpin turns.

The consequence of such an attraction process would be the imposition of a form of order on the otherwise random motions and locations of the floating molecules of nucleic acid. Each long and stretched-out surface-bound nucleic acid molecule would catch and hold nearby floating molecules in disciplined alignment, with the particular order of the different types of floating individuals being that required to provide a series of matches between the base sequences of the bound molecule and those of the hairpin-curved ends of the floating molecules (Fig. 11-3). Although modern evidence suggests that a relatively small number

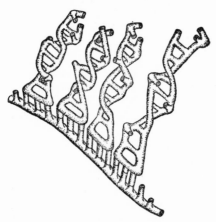

Fig. 11-3. Attachment of "floating" molecules of nucleic acid to a long "surface-bound" molecule.

of conjugated bases is available for the attachment of a single folded and twisted molecule (probably three), the resulting binding energy would probably be great enough to permit the displacement of most potentially interfering molecular fragments from the surface-bound molecule, including occasional conjugated nucleotides. To be sure, ambiguities could occur in the matching of folded to bound molecules. For example, several different types of folded molecule might have the same sequence of "connection" bases and therefore be interchangeable along the backbone of the surface-bound nucleic acid molecule. Nevertheless, on the average, the natural forces of interaction between bound and floating molecules would result in a strong tendency for a limited number of specific linear configurations to occur.*

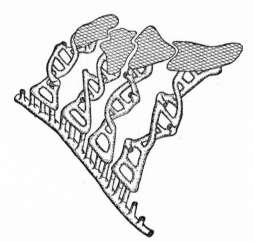

Fig. 11-4. Assembly of matching components of a "parasitic" molecule by the nucleic acid mechanisms. (Segments of parasitic molecule shown cross-hatched.)

* Figure 11-3 suggests a further kind of ambiguity: it would appear that the folded molecules could attach themselves to the surface-bound molecule either as shown, leaning over to the right, or in opposite orientation, leaning over toward the left. Such ambiguity is, however, only apparent,

But we have seen that the folded and twisted molecules are often the keepers of pets—that different types of such molecules are likely to be found clutching different kinds of molecular fragments picked up from the surrounding fluid. Therefore, any tendency for these floating nucleic acid molecules to align themselves in an ordered array must imply a corresponding tendency for the parasitic molecular fragments to be similarly aligned. This could have interesting consequences. Suppose, for example, that the orderly alignment imposed by the control of the surface-bound nucleic acid molecule results in bringing together several parasitic fragments that are capable of combining to form a stable large molecule (Fig. 11-4). Under such circumstances the production of this kind of large molecule is bound to occur much more rapidly than would be possible under purely random conditions; for the limitation on the rate of formation of complex molecules is usually the rarity of suitable encounters among its several components.

Here, finally, is a nucleic-acid-dependent phenomenon capable of survival value. For the species of "parasitic" complex molecule for whose accelerated assembly the nucleic acid mechanisms are responsible could be important to the primary metabolism of the host cell. If so, cells equipped with a combination of the mechanisms we have described and a starting quantity of nucleic acid molecules of the particular types required to promote the manufacture of the parasitic ingredient in question would grow more rapidly than other cells not so equipped. *In accordance with the simple economics of evolution, this could ultimately result in a predominance of the favorably endowed organisms and in the ascendancy of the nucleic acid mechanisms to a position of importance in the control of growth and reproduction.*

---

not real. The hydrogen bonds that join the conjugate bases of the folded and surface-bound molecules can be established only for one of the two possible orientations of the folded molecules.

With this conclusion we have reached a most important stage in our speculation on the origin of the nucleic acid mechanisms. Let us briefly review the argument to this point and make sure that, in retrospect, it seems plausible.

We started with a brief consideration of the molecular structure of nucleic acid—the repetitive backbone segments that hook together to form long chains and the side chains, or bases, that bestow individuality on the different segments of the molecule. We also reminded ourselves of the evidence of an earlier chapter for the automatic formation of simple nucleic acid molecules under the conditions that prevailed at the earth's surface several billion years ago.

In commencing our attempt to reconstruct the chemical adventures participated in by nucleic acid molecules during the late coacervate period of evolving life, our attention was directed to the small number of different side chains appearing in nucleic acid—4 instead of the 20 of protein construction. We also found ourselves at an early stage considering the consequences of the fact that in nucleic acid not only the backbone segments but also the side chains or bases have a tendency to hook together in certain ways. In particular, we learned that the unattached end of the base that projects from each nucleotide of the backbone of a nucleic acid molecule has an affinity for the corresponding end of the base projecting from one of the three other types of nucleotide. We learned, further, that the resulting two-base configurations all have about the same overall length. This coincidence, we found, permits the joining together of the sugar phosphate ends of the "captured" nucleotides, resulting in the formation of a new and complete nucleic acid molecule "complementary" to the original one and tied to it in Siamese-twin fashion.

To separate our new double-stranded molecule into two single-stranded pieces of nucleic acid, we postulated a time-varying metabolic cycle that would from time to time introduce into the fluid of the host coacervate or cell a quantity of catalyst or other ingredient capable of breaking the relatively weak hydrogen bonds holding the two strands together. Cyclical repetition of the two-stage process—accretion of nucleotides to single-stranded molecules to form double-stranded ones, followed by splitting of the double molecules—was assumed to occur continuously and automatically as a natural consequence of the postulated time-varying metabolism. The result was a "nucleic acid factory" in the cell, with a steady output of molecules exactly like those originally present in the cellular fluid together with a corresponding output of molecules with a base sequence "complementary" to the original nucleic acid.

We next considered some of the activities of the single-stranded nucleic acid molecules other than those related to reproduction. Without introducing major new postulates, we were able to see that the strong base-pairing affinity of nucleic acid, together with the flexibility of its backbone, would naturally lead to the appearance of certain kinds of folded and twisted molecules. We concluded also that some of the longer varieties of nucleic acid would be able to "lie down" in stretched-out position on membranes or solid inclusions that might be found in the cell. We were, of course, helped to these conclusions by experimental evidence for the existence in the fluid of modern cells of various types of folded and twisted molecules of the general nature described, as well as by evidence for the surface binding of extended nucleic acid molecules on the cellular microsomes.

Given the "surface-bound" and "floating" forms of nucleic acid to which we had been led by our combination of speculation and experimental evidence, two further deductions came easily. One consisted of the inference that some of our folded and twisted floating molecules of nucleic acid would probably possess three-dimensional configurations of electric charge that would provide an effective fit for other kinds of molecular fragments found in the cellular fluid; this led us to the idea that a specific type of floating nucleic acid molecule, with a characteristic folded and twisted configuration determined by the sequence of bases that embellish its backbone, would frequently carry enmeshed in its coils an equally specific "parasite," such as a particular sugar or amino acid. The second deduction arose as one more consequence of the base-pairing affinity of nucleic acid: at the horseshoe bend of the folded nucleic acid molecule, limitations on the flexibility of the backbone must result in leaving several successive unpaired bases protruding from the structure; if this end of the floating molecule were to approach a region of a surface-bound nucleic acid molecule where there just happened to be a sequence of several bases complementary to the horseshoe sequence, the floating molecule would stick to the surface-bound molecule.

From these two deductions we finally reached our important conclusion as to the architectural capabilities of the nucleic acid mechanisms: each cell contains specific types of long surface-bound and shorter floating molecules of nucleic acid; the specificity of the floating molecules is matched by a corresponding specificity in the parasitic molecular fragments to which they become bound as they float about in the cellular fluid; the particular sequences of unpaired bases at the horseshoe bends direct the different types of floating molecules to complementary regions of the surface-bound molecules; this in turn lines up the various types of parasitic fragments in an order that is determined by the specific base sequence of the surface-bound nucleic acid; the resulting juxtaposition then facilitates the hooking together of some of the parasitic fragments to form more complex molecules; a fortuitous set of relationships among the base sequences of the bound molecules, those of the horseshoe bends of the floating molecules, and the specific parasitic affinities of the floating molecules occasionally results in a "factory" producing substan-

tial quantities of a type of parasitic molecule of importance to the
cellular growth processes; when this happens, the happily
equipped cell and its progeny possess an advantage in the continuing evolutionary battle for species survival; as a consequence,
cells embodying the new nucleic acid mechanisms become con-
spicuously numerous among the organisms of the earth.

BIBLIOGRAPHY

Beadle, G. W., "The New Genetics," in 1964 *Britannica Book of the
Year* (Encyclopaedia Britannica, Inc., Chicago, 1964), pp. 45–72.

Doty, P., "The Relation of the Interaction of Polynucleotides to the
Secondary Structure of Nucleic Acids," in *The Structure and Bio-
synthesis of Macromolecules,* ed. by Bell and Grant (Cambridge
University Press, London, England, 1962), pp. 8–28.

Fresco, J. R., "Some Investigations in the Secondary and Tertiary
Structure of Ribonucleic Acids," in *Informational Macromolecules,*
ed. by Vogel, Bryson, and Lampen (Academic Press Inc., New
York, 1963), pp. 121–142.

Herskowitz, I. H., *Genetics* (Little, Brown and Company, Boston,
1962), chap. 47, "Gene Action and Amino Acid Coding."

chapter 12

Refinement of the Nucleic Acid Mechanisms

It is clear that the nucleic acid mechanisms for the control of growth and reproduction that have been described to this point contain a number of imperfections. For example, the existence in the cell of several different types of floating molecules with the same arrangement of unpaired bases at the hairpin bend would permit the same kind of surface-bound nucleic acid molecule to control the assembly of more than one kind of array of parasitic molecular fragments. The same result could arise from certain kinds of interferences among the floating molecules: the early attachment of one such molecule at a complementary region of the surface-bound nucleic acid might render impossible the later attachment of another floating molecule if suitable conjugation of its "connection" bases should require that it occupy almost the same position as the earlier arrival. Because of the high probability that only one of the resulting arrays would lead to the forma-

125

tion of a complex molecule that would be useful in the metabolism of the host cell, this kind of architectural unpredictability would usually result in lowering the survival value of the associated mechanisms.

Similarly, in the geometry of the alignment of parasitic fragments there would appear to be extensive opportunities for inefficiency. Depending on the exact three-dimensional configurations of the floating nucleic acid molecules, the successive parasitic fragments that need to combine to form the complex product molecule might be twisted or displaced relative to one another; this could greatly diminish the probability that they would make the necessary linkages.

But these are just the kinds of problem that evolution must have found it easy to solve. For by the slow but inexorable workings of natural selection the initially crude and imperfect processes would have been gradually refined. Improvement in the ability of the floating molecules to align their parasitic fragments for ease of coupling probably started, for example, in an accidental change or "mutation" in the structure of one of the floating molecules of some individual. If the change was a lucky one, it would have caused the floating molecule to hold the parasitic fragment it carried in a better position or orientation for linkage with its neighbors. As a result the host individual would have grown more rapidly and produced more progeny; the new descendants, possessing the improved nucleic acid molecule, would in turn have thrived by comparison with their less well-endowed fellows. Ultimately the new species would have displaced the old; the modified kind of nucleic acid would have become "standard equipment."

We can even trace at least part of the evolutionary development that has tended to reduce the architectural unpredictability that would have resulted from competition of different types of floating molecules for affiliation with overlapping bases of the stretched-out molecules. Bishop, Leahy, and Schweet, of the City of Hope in Los Angeles, and Dintzis, of the Massachusetts Institute of Technology, discovered an interesting refinement in the processes involved when floating and surface-bound molecules come together. Using radioactively tagged amino acid components, these investigators were able to show that the floating molecules attach themselves one at a time along the surface-bound molecule, moving from one end to the other—in order, like strung beads. It therefore appears that in modern cells one end of the long surface-bound nucleic acid molecule carries an arrangement of electric charge that interacts with part of the appropriate floating molecule so as to provide an especially tight bond for its attachment. In turn, once the appropriate floating molecule attaches itself tightly to this end position of the surface-bound molecule, its presence results in increasing the strength with which the next floating molecule can be attached to the growing structure, and so on. In addition to eliminating some of the possibilities for manufacture of the "wrong" parasitic molecule, this refinement, through the additional strength of the connections between surface-bound and floating molecules, enhances the ability of the floating molecules to displace "impurities" tenuously attached to the surface-bound template.

Thus, by means of countless small evolutionary steps, the nucleic acid mechanisms have been refined until little remains today of the erraticism and inefficiency that must once have characterized their fumbling architectural efforts. Although experimental evidence is less than complete, there is reason to believe that all the floating nucleic acid molecules that appear in modern organisms are well designed in the sense that they couple tightly to the structure provided by the surface-bound and previously attached floating molecules and position their parasitic fragments properly for easy linkage with their neighbors. In addition, modern combinations of floating and surface-bound nucleic acid molecules appear to be unambiguously coded in the sense that a surface-bound molecule of specified base sequence always directs the formation of one and only one kind of parasitic complex molecule.

One of the important evolutionary developments that occurred somewhere along the line was the appearance in single-celled organisms of a division of effort between the two types of nucleic acid, RNA and DNA. In modern organisms it is only DNA that exhibits the two-stage self-reproduction process described in Chapter 10. For the most part, this is carried out in the principle cellular "inclusion," the *nucleus.** In fact, this DNA never leaves the nucleus. Instead, the DNA molecules manufacture complementary RNA molecules, which then leave the nucleus and carry out in the surrounding cellular regions—the *cytoplasm*—the architectural activities that we have previously considered. The base sequence in an RNA molecule manufactured in this way is, of course, determined by the base sequence of the generating DNA molecule, with the A, G, C, and T bases of the DNA "template" matched by U, C, G, and A bases, respectively, along the backbone of the RNA "product." †

The nature of the processes connecting DNA and RNA

---

* As we shall learn in the next chapter, recent work has revealed that a small amount of DNA activity also occurs in other cellular inclusions.

† The formation of RNA depends upon a highly sophisticated type of catalytic action. The DNA molecules in the nucleus are always double-stranded (except for short intervals when they are reproducing themselves). From time to time a catalytic molecule attaches itself to the double-stranded DNA and breaks some of the hydrogen bonds so as to spread apart a section of the two strands. This permits nucleotides appropriate to RNA to aggregate to one (only one!) of the separated strands. But as this happens, the changing electric forces cause the catalytic molecule to move along the DNA, successively separating new regions of the double molecule. This, in turn, permits the newly exposed part of the active strand of DNA to attract additional nucleotides and add new

gives rise to descriptive names for the surface-bound and floating RNA of our discussion. The first type is commonly called *messenger RNA* in recognition of its role of transcribing from a DNA molecule in the nucleus a "message" determining the architecture of the parasitic molecule whose assembly is ultimately to be directed by the RNA molecule. The accepted term for what we have called floating RNA is *transfer RNA* * in recognition of its role in transferring parasitic molecular fragments into ordered alignment under the direction of a molecule of messenger RNA.

It is, of course, the key importance of the nucleus as the habitat of the DNA and the place of manufacture of the RNA that originally gave rise to the term "nucleic acid." And of the two kinds of nucleic acid, the division of effort we have just described assigns to DNA a sort of primacy. The loss or destruction of any of the RNA molecules can be compensated for by the generation of new RNA under the architectural supervision of the DNA. But the cell can never compensate for the absence of any of the

---

segments to the matching RNA molecule. Meanwhile, as the catalyst and the site of active RNA synthesis move along the double-stranded DNA molecule, the separated strands close in again behind the action, stripping off the newly formed RNA and restoring the double-stranded configuration of the DNA.

In terms of our speculations as to the origins of the nucleic acid mechanisms, such complex processes must be considered to be the result of extensive evolutionary refinements that make of the modern cell a much more advanced organism than the late coacervate/early cellular structures we have heretofore imagined. It is probable that the structural separation of the parts of modern cells (nucleus and cytoplasm in most cells; less pronounced but nonetheless important structural details in bacteria and other primitive organisms) contributes to the sophistication of the nucleic acid mechanisms by facilitating differences in the catalytic and other chemical content of different parts of the cellular fluid.

* Sometimes also called *soluble RNA* because of the ability of these short molecules to remain in fluid suspension.

types of DNA molecule on which its metabolism depends. These molecules must come to the cell from its parent in the course of cell division. Subsequently, only the *numbers* of DNA molecules of the available types may increase by the duplication process we have studied; new *types* cannot be formed (except, of course, by an occasional accidental mutation). Clearly it is DNA, not RNA, that contains in the base patterns of its molecules the original book of instructions for the chemistry of the cell.

But of all the evolutionary refinements that we can deduce must have taken place in the nucleic acid mechanisms one seems to have overshadowed all others in its importance. This far-reaching development consisted of a specialization in the nature of the parasitic complex molecules for whose architecture the nucleic acid mechanisms were responsible. With the passage of time the specific structures of the controlling DNA molecules in the nucleus and of the resulting messenger and transfer RNA in the cytoplasm were gradually modified until finally the cytoplasmic "factory" controlled by the nucleic acid mechanisms came to manufacture only one general class of product. This class of product consists in its entirety of protein material—primarily of protein material having special catalytic properties. These protein catalysts, called *enzymes,* play a key role in the metabolism of all modern living organisms. In order to comprehend the strength of the tendency that impelled the forces of natural selection to eliminate other products of the nucleic acid mechanisms in favor of enzymes, we must first learn something of the nature of these protein catalysts and of the powerful role they play in life processes.

We may start our digression by reminding ourselves that, in much of the analysis and speculation that has brought us to this point, we have relied heavily on the action of catalytic substances to render plausible the degree of chemical reactivity that our theories have required. We have been encouraged to do so by the extensive evidence that common atomic ingredients combined into spatial configurations of types found in living organisms do frequently display the remarkable accelerating effects on chemical processes that the term "catalyst" implies. The important new element that must be injected into the discussion at this point is the fact that, of all organic catalysts, none can compare in effectiveness with certain kinds of protein. It appears that the "tangled string" design of the protein molecule, described in Chapter 4, is ideally suited to the catalytic function—at least for the catalysis of reactions involving other organic material. The complex surface of such a molecule, with its specific exposed regions of positive and negative electric charge, can provide a sort of template into which molecules of other types can fit. If the surface arrangement of positive and negative charges on the protein molecule corresponds closely to the distribution of negative and positive charges on another organic molecule, there will be specific affinity for that molecule. If the correspondence is good but not perfect, the strains developed when the attracted molecule "sits down" on the protein may break some of the bonds that hold it together so that, when other arriving material displaces that temporarily adsorbed to the protein, fragments of the original molecule, rather than the whole molecule itself, are sent back into the surrounding fluid. This is the way our digestive enzymes work to break down the organic materials we take in as food into the essential amino acids and other structural units from which new forms of molecular arrangements suitable to the human architecture can be built up. In this subsequent reconstruction other enzymes are employed, each possessing surface electric fields that attract and force into juxtaposition the specific molecular fragments needed to make up the particular kind of complex molecule whose construction supervision is the enzyme's reason for existence. Probably millions of different kinds of enzyme operate today to control the complex chemistry of plants and animals. In addition to their abundance and versatility, enzymes are amazingly powerful. Thus, the digestive processes in our stomachs cause the disintegration of the food we eat much faster than would the strongest concentration of acid, without the destructive effect on the stomach lining that the acid would have.

Returning to the chemical production lines operated by the nucleic acid mechanisms, let us now compare the metabolic effectiveness of two possible products of these mechanisms. One product might be a certain carbohydrate required at some stage of the cell's chemistry; the other product, however, might be a protein enzyme that would amplify the rate of production of that same carbohydrate through some otherwise unimportant secondary chain of cellular reactions. Which product would contribute more to the cell's growth? The answer would depend, of course, on the initial productivity of the "unimportant secondary chain of cellular reactions" and on the amount of multiplication of that productivity caused by the protein enzyme. But we know from modern research that the second factor can be tremendous —multiplication of billions in the rate of reaction is easily possible for a well-designed enzyme. When this is considered in conjunction with the almost limitless variety of chemical reactions that are possible among the organic and inorganic ingredients of a living cell, it is easy to imagine that nucleic acid molecules with a structure contributing to protein enzyme manufacture might have more of an impact on the growth and reproduction rates of the host organism than molecules leading to the direct, noncatalytic production of the structural materials of the cell. And evidently this is a correct conclusion; it appears to account for the fact that modern nucleic acid mechanisms manufacture only proteins, nothing else.* The protein enzymes, which today are

---

* However, it is not quite true that the nucleic acid mechanisms manufacture only enzymes. Some structural proteins, which may not have catalytic properties, are also produced. This does not upset the strength

highly specific and very powerful owing to their precisely tailored structure, then exercise tight control over all the complex chemistry of the living cell. Thus the mechanisms we have been studying truly constitute the genesis of the properties of the cell they serve. They are quite properly referred to as the *genetic mechanisms*.

It is important that some of the implications of the specialization on protein manufacture should be understood. For example, the DNA molecules in the nucleus that are responsible for the production of transfer RNA have evolved such a sequence of bases as to manufacture only types of floating molecules possessing special affinity for the amino acids. Since 20 different amino acids enter into the formation of proteins, the cytoplasm of every living cell possesses 20 different kinds of transfer RNA.* Similarly, the DNA molecules in the nucleus that are responsible for the production of messenger RNA have evolved in such a way as to manufacture only types of surface-bound molecules whose base sequences conjugate with the unpaired connection bases of the transfer molecules that carry the amino acids. The result is a protein factory in the cytoplasm.

For establishing the one-to-one correspondence between DNA molecules in the nucleus and enzymes manufactured in the cytoplasm, G. W. Beadle and E. L. Tatum, then at Stanford University, shared in the Nobel Prize in Physiology and Medicine in 1958. Later discoveries have somewhat modified their conclusions but in no way detracted from the pioneering importance of their

---

of the evolutionary argument, however, for noncatalytic proteins could obviously be assembled as by-products of mechanisms developed for enzyme manufacture.

* As we shall learn in the next chapter, there are in fact more than 20: several types of transfer RNA molecule may be capable of transporting the same amino acid. This does not cause trouble in the assembly of the enzyme, for the messenger RNA molecule is coded unambiguously in terms of the various transfer RNAs.

work. We have already noted that sometimes nonenzymatic proteins are ordered into existence by the nucleic acid mechanisms. In addition, it now appears that a DNA molecule is frequently responsible for the construction of only a major segment of a protein and that the final stage of protein assembly consists of a joining together in the cytoplasm of two or more such segments. However, despite its slight inaccuracy, the description originally applied to the work of Beadle and Tatum—"one DNA molecule,* one enzyme"—still characterizes its most important implications.

Because of their great chemical accelerating power, it is not surprising to find that the enzymes have come to play a role not only in the general metabolism of the cell but in the operation of the underlying genetic mechanisms themselves. The catalysts we have postulated to assist in the formation of double-stranded from single-stranded nucleic acid are, in modern organisms, protein enzymes. And the related production of messenger RNA by DNA in the nucleus proceeds at a negligible rate unless an enzyme, *RNA-polymerase,* is present. Similarly, the attachment of an amino acid to a molecule of transfer RNA in the cytoplasm involves the intermediation of an enzyme.† There is, in fact, a different such "attachment" enzyme for each of the 20 different amino acids. Finally, when the amino acids have been aligned along the controlling messenger RNA molecule, another enzyme links them together and in the process detaches the resulting pro-

* Beadle and Tatum actually established the connection between *genes* and enzymes. Later work (see Chap. 14) showed the identity of genes and DNA molecules.

† There is a little more to this process than simple "attachment." Energy must also be supplied by the participation of a molecule of adenosine triphosphate (ATP), which is abundant in the cytoplasm. This results in the temporary addition to the amino acid of an energy-rich fragment which, however, drops off when the amino acids are finally linked to form a protein molecule under the guidance of the messenger RNA.

tein molecule and sends it out into the surrounding fluid so that it can later perform its own important catalytic function in some possibly remote region of the cell.

This, then, completes our story of how the powerful nucleic acid/enzyme control mechanisms might have got started. As pointed out in Chapter 9, there are too many successive and un-verified assumptions in the story for it to have any great likeli-hood of being true in detail, although the properties finally achieved by the postulated evolutionary processes are known to be those of the genetic mechanisms of modern organisms. Fortu-nately, in terms of the objectives of this treatment, the accuracy of the evolutionary description is not critical. The important thing is that the recital given here should carry conviction as to the adequacy of purely physical processes of the general nature of those postulated to account for the evolution of the modern cellular mechanisms.

But we have not yet completed our consideration of the nucleic acid/enzyme mechanisms; we are merely taking note of a transi-tion in the character of the discussion. From a treatment combin-ing a very large proportion of speculation with only occasional experimental support we now revert to a more orthodox mixture of extensive experimental findings and modest speculative con-tent. Chapter 13 will complete our discussion of the genetic mechanisms by such a treatment of the evidence of recent re-search for a remarkable universality of many of the details as well as the general features of these mechanisms.

BIBLIOGRAPHY

Asimov, I., *The Genetic Code* (The Orion Press, Inc., New York, 1962), chap. 9, "The Cooperating Strands," and chap. 11, "Break-ing the Code."

Beadle, G. W., "The New Genetics," in 1964 *Britannica Book of the Year* (Encyclopaedia Britannica, Inc., Chicago, 1964), pp. 45–72.

Bishop, J. O., J. Leahy, and R. S. Schweet, *Proceedings of the National Academy of Sciences,* vol. 46 (1960), p. 1030.

Haurowitz, F., *The Chemistry and Function of Proteins* (Academic Press Inc., New York, 1963), chap. 16, "Protein Biosynthesis."

Herskowitz, I. H., *Genetics* (Little, Brown and Company, Boston, 1962), chap. 47, "Gene Action and Amino Acid Coding."

chapter 13

The Proliferation
of Successful Techniques:
Biological Standardization

In our development of the genetic mechanisms there has been a conspicuous absence of qualifying statements such as "this is the way it works in the frog" or "the bacterial mechanisms look like this." On the contrary, in several aspects of the preceding treatment it has been implied, and occasionally it has been specifically stated, that in the nucleic acid/enzyme mechanisms we seem to be dealing with a general biological principle applicable equally to amoeba or man. But it would obviously be unreasonable to imagine that a mechanism as complex as that underlying the interplay between the giant molecules of nucleic acid and protein enzymes could have been independently developed for each of many different species by the tortuous processes of evolution. Therefore, if the nucleic acid/enzyme mechanisms do indeed exist in all forms of modern organisms, it would seem necessary to conclude that they originated early in the history of life—before much progress had been made in the evolutionary differentiation that has resulted in today's large variety of living forms—and that they subsequently survived in all of those forms only because their possession proved to contribute to all types of host organism markedly superior survival attributes. This hypothesis credits a single evolutionary discovery with such remarkably superior properties as to justify us in requiring of the biologists some rather strong evidence before we accept the current doctrine of the ubiquity of the nucleic acid/enzyme mechanisms. Let us therefore look at some of the recent research findings that suggest that we are here in fact dealing with a universal biological principle.

Of course, the first discoveries attesting to the existence of the nucleic acid/enzyme control mechanisms could provide little evidence for their generality. Indeed, nearly all of the early work was done on bacteria or other microorganisms. It was not until 1962, for example, that messenger RNA was isolated from mammalian cells. However, unspecific, but highly suggestive, evidence pointing toward the broad applicability of the new discoveries was easy to come by. For example, DNA is always discovered in cell nuclei, when it is looked for. Similarly, the cytoplasm is always found to contain microsomes and RNA. And protein enzymes have been shown to control the chemical processes that occur in the wide variety of plant and animal cells that have been investigated.

One of the strongest reasons for believing that the nucleic acid/enzyme mechanisms might constitute a general principle of life was the neat solution they provided for a long-standing mystery of biochemistry—the precise architecture of protein molecules. A reasonable explanation of how, in nature, as distinct from the laboratory of the chemist, hundreds or thousands of different amino acid segments could be strung together in precisely ordered arrays, as was known to be required by the remarkable structure sensitivity of the enzyme molecules, filled a tremendous gap in biological theory. For this reason the notion that all forms of living cells employ a system of control of their chemical processes of the general nature of that described in the preceding chapters has from the first been attractive to biologists.

But no matter how attractive a theory might be, no good scientist would fail to put it to experimental test. And it was clearly important to do more than merely confirm the employment by various plant and animal species of similar broad principles of metabolic and genetic control. For the hypothesis that all living cells are controlled in their chemistry by a mechanism involving the interaction of nucleic acid and enzyme molecules, even if true, clearly need not imply identity in the *details* of the mechanisms employed by different organisms. Any ingenious scientist would encounter little difficulty in inventing variations of the nuclear DNA/messenger RNA/transfer RNA/microsome/protein enzyme scheme we have "derived" that would appear, from all that is known today, to be as workable as the particular scheme described. Thus an inevitable preoccupation of the research scientists has had to be not only to look for the existence of nucleic acid/enzyme mechanisms in various species but also to determine the extent of variation in these mechanisms from species to species.

Determination of the similarities and differences among the molecular mechanisms of different species of organisms is not as easy as it sounds, however. Scientific techniques are not yet advanced to the point where molecules of DNA in the nucleus or RNA in the cytoplasm can be sorted out and their precise dimensions and structure catalogued. As is so usual in science, indirect methods of throwing light on the question at hand had to be sought.

When considered in terms of modern knowledge, an experiment performed in 1928 seems to have first pointed the way toward a suitable investigative technique. That early experiment involved work with a certain type of pneumonia-causing bacterium. It had been found that this bacterium comes in two slightly different forms, or "strains." One strain is characterized by a smooth coating surrounding the bacterial cell; this is called the smooth, or S, strain. Bacteria of the other strain possess no such coating. They are called the rough, or R, strain. The curious thing that was reported in 1928 about these two strains of bacteria was that, when a batch of dead S bacteria was added to living R bacteria, there would subsequently appear in the culture living members of the S strain. (It had been well established that a colony composed exclusively of R bacteria would produce only more R types, whereas S bacteria would also breed true.) Since it was inconceivable that dead S bacteria could come back to life, the 1928 experiment had always required the conclusion that something in the dead S bacteria had converted some live R bacteria into live S bacteria. Many years later, additional experiments succeeded in isolating this something and showing that it was pure nucleic acid.* In terms of our present understanding of the nucleic acid mechanisms, the explanation of the behavior of the pneumococci is not difficult. Evidently the S bacteria contain a molecule of DNA that, through the mechanisms we have studied, leads to the formation of an enzyme that results in the construction of the smooth coating that characterizes this particular strain. A bacterium of the R strain differs from one of the S strain in not possessing this particular piece of DNA. The treatment that killed the S bacteria did not destroy their DNA. When the live R bacteria were mixed with dead S bacteria, occasionally

* This discovery was made in 1944 by three Rockefeller Institute biochemists, Oswald T. Avery, Colin M. McLeod, and Maclyn McCarty. The first demonstration of the DNA nature of genetic material, it played a major role in stimulating the upsurge in studies on nucleic acid.

DNA from a dead cell was able to work its way into a living cell, thereby supplying the kind of nucleic acid needed for the formation of a smooth coat. Result: the R bacterium became an S bacterium instead.

Clearly, this experiment constituted a step toward the establishment of generality in the genetic mechanisms; for it showed that the DNA from one type of pneumococcus bacterium could successfully operate the complex messenger RNA/transfer RNA/microsome apparatus of the other type of bacteria to produce a new and effective enzyme molecule. To be sure, if our theories are any good at all, they would have to account for the similarity of the genetic mechanisms among organisms so closely related as two strains of the same bacterial type. Nevertheless, the experiment was a step in the right direction. It suggested further steps. Was it possible to devise more advanced experiments to test for a similar kind of operation of the genetic mechanisms of one species by the nucleic acid from an entirely *unrelated* species of organism? Such a phenomenon, if it could be observed, would imply considerable similarity in the details as well as the general characteristics of the nucleic acid/enzyme mechanisms of unrelated species.

It has indeed been found possible to devise experiments to test the proposed hypothesis. It is virus research that has provided this possibility. This work is important enough to our story to justify our digressing to study the characteristics of virus particles that are pertinent to an understanding of some of its implications.

A virus particle is the simplest of all living * structures. It consists of only two components: a quantity of nucleic acid surrounded by a shell, or "overcoat," of protein material. There is no

* The applicability of this adjective is questioned by many. The peculiar combination of living and nonliving attributes that characterizes viruses will become evident as the discussion progresses.

cellular structure—no nucleus, no cytoplasm, no microsomes, none of the other complex structures that we shall later see make of the modern living cell a complex piece of machinery. By itself, a virus particle appears to be a lifeless object: it does not eat, grow, reproduce or die; no chemical processes take place in its vitals; it is an inert capsule of protein-protected nucleic acid. Certain virus particles may even form regular crystalline matrices, yielding microscopic structures of overall mechanical and optical properties grossly similar to those of salt or diamond, for example. In terms of such properties, viruses appear much more akin to lifeless minerals than to living organisms.

But put virus particles in contact with living cells of a suitable species of plant or animal and the situation changes dramatically. For now, life seems to appear. In a matter of minutes the number of virus particles will have doubled. Under suitable conditions, a few hours will suffice for a millionfold increase in their population!

This peculiar lifelike/nonlifelike dichotomy in the personality of the virus has caused considerable attention to be focused on it in recent years. Without doubt, Wendell M. Stanley heads the list of pioneers in the field. As early as 1935 he showed that the *tobacco mosaic virus* (TMV), which causes the disease of the tobacco leaf, could be isolated in the form of pure crystals. For his work in this field, Stanley shared in the 1946 Nobel Prize in Chemistry.

Stanley's pioneering work on the tobacco mosaic virus led to studies by many investigators of the curious reproductive processes of viruses. Some of the interesting discoveries have been made with the kinds of viruses that attack, and therefore reproduce in, plant cells—such as those studied by Stanley; other important discoveries have arisen out of work with the so-called *bacteriophages*—viruses that attack and reproduce in the cells of bacteria. A consistent picture has emerged from all of this work bearing on the way in which a virus particle is able to make use of the genetic mechanisms of the cell it infects in order to reproduce its own kind.

The virus story is so strange that it is worthwhile to point out that it rests today on very firm experimental evidence. Some of the important episodes in the reproductive process of bacterial and certain other viruses can in fact be "seen" by means of the electron microscope. The first episode of the sequence is of this nature: the attachment by certain virus particles to the outer surface of the cell to be attacked. The next step can be deduced from later developments: apparently there is an enzyme in the protein coat of the virus particle which dissolves a hole in the membrane of the cell to which it is attached. The products of the chemical reactions involved then cause the entire protein capsule to contract. This has the effect of a hypodermic injection—squirting the nucleic acid content of the virus particle into the interior of the cell that is being infected.

All this is remarkable enough, but what follows is even more spectacular. For the invading nucleic acid proceeds to take over from the cellular DNA and redirect the internal chemistry of the invaded organism! First, the viral nucleic acid directs the manufacture of enzymes that attack the cellular DNA, thereby destroying the "control center" of the victim. Then a period of rapid reproduction of the viral nucleic acid begins. A little later, the viral nucleic acid induces the production of the kind of protein needed to make the protective covering of additional virus particles. After a few more minutes the newly formed strands of viral nucleic acid begin to get together with the new protein overcoats to form complete new virus particles. Eventually, when this assembly process has gone to completion, the last command is given by the invader to the cellular mechanisms—this time to produce an enzyme that dissolves large holes in the external membrane of the cell and allows the newly formed virus particles to escape.

Between the instant of initial attachment by a virus particle to the healthy cell and the final cataclysmic disintegration, twenty or thirty minutes elapse. The end product of the remarkable sequence of chemical steps is several hundred newborn virus particles, each identical with the one which started the chain of activity and each capable of initiating a similar lethal sequence in another healthy cell.

In view of their bizarre reproductive habits, it is easy to understand the fascination that viruses hold for biologists. However, we must confine our attention to the light we earlier predicted virus studies would throw on the generality of the nucleic acid/enzyme mechanisms. It is, of course, the ability of the viral nucleic acid to take over and successfully redirect the metabolic processes in the invaded cell that is pertinent to our theories. For, even in the absence of present knowledge as to all the details of the interaction, it seems clear that the virus-reproduction story implies great compatibility between the design of the virus nucleic acid and the nucleic acid/enzyme mechanisms of the host cell. The invading nucleic acid is not only able to reproduce itself in the cell but also able to provide messenger RNA that successfully attaches itself to the cellular microsomes and directs the formation of virus-specific enzymes. For this purpose transfer RNA, amino acid fragments, phosphate energizers, and a number of enzymes must come into play. Because of the relative simplicity of the viral nucleic acid molecules, it seems unlikely that new forms of all such components are synthesized under their direction; rather, it seems that the specifically virus messenger RNA must be able to work in conjunction with components indigenous to the healthy cell in the manufacture of the enzymes needed for the formation of new virus particles.

Thus virus research, in establishing the remarkable compatibility of the genetic mechanisms of forms of life so different as those of bacteria and viruses, has further strengthened the argument for the universality of these mechanisms. However, just as in the case of the pneumococci results, the evidence is less than conclusive. After all, viruses are pretty specific, each limited in its destructive ability to only one or a few species of cells. This is indicated by the descriptive labels given to viruses: the *tobacco mosaic virus,* the *turnip yellows mosaic virus,* the *rabbit papilloma virus,* and so on. Therefore we cannot ignore the possibility that, just as with the R and S strains of pneumococci, there is a close evolutionary kinship between the virus and the cell it attacks. Perhaps the two organisms, though greatly dissimilar, developed symbiotically through the ages in such a way as to maintain compatibility among their nuclear control mechanisms. When thought of in this way, it could be that the virus and its related cell constitute a sort of single two-part organism and that the seemingly remarkable ability of the one to operate the chemical machinery of the other is but a prosaic example of the inevitable internal consistency in the metabolism of a viable organism, with no implications as to the universality of the genetic mechanisms among really different species.

Of course, we go a bit too far in disclaiming all pertinence to our thesis of the virus results. For a single virus sometimes does attack more than one cell species. After all, monkeys as well as men can contract polio. Just as in the case of the pneumococci results, nothing can keep the virus work from being suggestive. However, we have not yet made a convincing case for the hypothesis that the genetic mechanisms are truly universal. More evidence is needed.

And there is more evidence. It came, between 1961 and 1963, out of the laboratories of the National Institutes of Health and the California Institute of Technology. In that interval Marshall

W. Nirenberg and J. Heinrich Matthaei, government research scientists at Bethesda, Maryland, and James Bonner and coworkers, at Pasadena, California, made some remarkable discoveries. Their findings are directly pertinent to our quest for evidence of the universality of the genetic mechanisms.

Both groups of investigators employed the lowliest of instruments in their important work—the *Escherichia coli* bacillus, a form of bacteria that thrives in the intestines of man and other vertebrates. They studied extracts from *E. coli* bacilli that contained microsomes, transfer RNA, energy-supplying phosphates, amino acids, and enzymes. When supplied with *E. coli* messenger RNA, such cell-free mixtures of essential ingredients were known to be capable of manufacturing proteins through the operation of the nucleic acid/enzyme mechanisms that we have been considering for the past several chapters. Nirenberg and Matthaei discovered, however, that the addition of big-molecular RNA from a number of other species, including viruses, could also cause protein to be synthesized.

The evidence that RNA molecules from one species could successfully act as messenger RNA in the protein-manufacturing mechanisms of an entirely unrelated species certainly added strength to the developing case for the universality of the genetic mechanisms. However, it also raised questions. For example, what *kind* of protein is produced when the big-molecular RNA from an exotic species is added to the *E. coli* system of components? Could it be protein characteristic of the species from which the big-molecular RNA is derived?

A number of experiments were performed in search of an answer to this question. In some the results were indeterminate, but in 1963 a definite, and affirmative, answer was obtained by the Caltech group. They combined purified DNA from the nuclei of pea cells with systems of *E. coli* components similar to those employed by Nirenberg and Matthaei and found that a kind of protein was produced that was specific to the particular type of pea cell from which the DNA had been extracted. Their results, in fact, went somewhat beyond the point of establishing that messenger RNA from pea cells could operate the nucleic acid mechanisms of *E. coli* bacilli to produce pea-cell protein. In addition, their work showed that pea-cell DNA could be induced to manufacture messenger RNA by the action of the enzyme *RNA-polymerase* derived from bacteria.

Here, finally, was an argument for the universality of the genetic mechanisms that was completely convincing. For no one could suggest that there was any special evolutionary kinship between the pea plant and the *Escherichia coli* bacillus that might cast doubt on the significance of the results. Nevertheless, pea-cell DNA had been found capable of operating the molecular mechanisms of *E. coli* not just to manufacture protein molecules, but to manufacture the precise type of protein molecules normally fabricated in the cells of pea plants. The experiment had demonstrated the existence in the pea plant and in the *E. coli* bacillus not only of grossly similar mechanisms but of mechanisms employing an identical "genetic code"—that is, an identical set of relationships connecting the sequence of bases along the backbone of the molecule of DNA and its messenger RNA, the particular kind of transfer RNA molecule attracted to each position along that backbone, and the particular kind of amino acid carried by each kind of transfer molecule. This was not just evidence for the existence in all cells of generally similar nucleic acid/enzyme control mechanisms; it was evidence for the existence of an impressive degree of detailed identity among the mechanisms of different organisms.

It would be misleading to leave the impression that serious consideration of the possibility of a single genetic code applicable to all cells originated with this work. From the first discovery that protein enzyme manufacture is controlled by the messenger

RNA/transfer RNA mechanisms there was much speculation about the kinds of code that might relate the sequence of bases along the messenger RNA molecule with the various kinds of transfer RNA in order to array the amino acid segments properly. Because it was the simplest assumption, the idea of only one such code for all cells was from the first a popular one. This does not in any way detract from the importance of the Nirenberg-Matthaei and Bonner discoveries, however, for theirs was the first convincing evidence that nature, as well as the biologists, had decided to make such a simplification.

But still another question was suggested to Nirenberg and Matthaei by their line of investigation: "If the addition of RNA from another organism to the nucleic acid/enzyme apparatus of the *E. coli* bacillus could stimulate the manufacture of protein products, what would happen if a synthetic RNA was added instead?" To be sure, the techniques available to Nirenberg and Matthaei caused their man-made product to fall far short of natural RNA in complexity of structure—they could not put nucleic acid molecules together with precisely known structure unless they contained, say, only one of the four bases. But, they reasoned, such simplicity might actually be an advantage in early attempts to study the details of the metabolic control processes. Therefore, they devised an experiment using the simplest possible kind of man-made RNA: *polyuridylic acid,* an RNA with the monotonous base sequence UUUUUUUUUUUU ⋯.

The experiment worked: the addition of synthetic RNA to the *E. coli* extracts resulted in the appearance of protein! A significant question, again, was: "What kind of protein?" There was considerable logical appeal in the answer, when it was finally provided by chemical analysis of the end product. For the protein whose construction was directed by the simplest possible kind of RNA was in turn the simplest possible kind of protein—a chain composed of a single amino acid, monotonously repeated. The particular kind of amino acid that was pulled out of the solution (which contained abundant supplies of all 20 amino acids) and incorporated into protein under the direction of the polyuridylic acid type of RNA turned out to be the amino acid *phenylalanine*.

Here was indeed an exciting discovery, for it constituted nothing less than a start toward the actual deciphering of the genetic code. Evidently the base sequence UUUUUUUUUUUU · · · in the messenger RNA was translated by the genetic mechanisms into the amino acid sequence phenylalanine, phenylalanine, phenylalanine, . . . in the resulting protein molecule. In Chapter 11 it has already been mentioned that, by a combination of experiment and theory, workers in the field had concluded it to be likely that each molecule of transfer RNA attaches to the messenger RNA by the conjugation of three pairs of bases. In terms of this hypothesis, and the known affinity of the U and A bases, the Nirenberg-Matthaei discovery was interpreted as implying that the particular kind of transfer RNA that carries the amino acid phenylalanine is characterized by a sequence of three unconjugated A bases at its hairpin bend.

The Nirenberg-Matthaei technique was quickly extended. For example, messenger RNA composed solely of *cytidylic acid* was found to cause the manufacture of protein molecules consisting entirely of the amino acid *proline*. More sophisticated experiments were also devised that employed synthetic RNA molecules containing a small amount of one of the other nucleotides in addition to uridylic acid.* Such messenger RNA in the *E. coli* extracts resulted in the production of protein products including not only phenylalanine but also occasional "intrusions" of other amino acids. By relating the frequency of occurrence of such other amino acids to the probabilities of occurrence in the RNA

---

* Techniques of synthesis permitted combining known *proportions* of the four nucleotides to form RNA, although the precise *sequence* of the nucleotides in the molecule remained unknown.

molecule of triplet combinations other than UUU, it was found possible to develop shrewd guesses as to many probable correspondences between specific messenger RNA triplet base sequences and specific resulting amino acids in the protein structure. And recently H. G. Khorana, of the University of Wisconsin, announced a technique whereby synthetic RNA molecules can be tailored to consist of a successive repetition along the backbone of known triads—UAU UAU UAU UAU UAU, for example. By the use of such molecules of messenger RNA in combination with the usual *E. coli* extracts, work is being speeded on the development of a dictionary connecting the various possible base triplets in messenger RNA with the particular amino acids that they are responsible for in the finally assembled protein molecules.

One of the interesting discoveries that has appeared in the course of all this work has to do with the *degeneracy* of the genetic code—the existence of several different sequences of bases in the messenger RNA molecule that can cause the same amino acid segment to be incorporated in the protein under construction. For example, the evidence strongly suggests that the amino acid *arginine* can be evoked by any one of the three messenger RNA triplets CGC, AGA, and UCG. The related inference also appears to be correct: that three different types of transfer RNA molecule, each capable of carrying the amino acid arginine, correspond to these three messenger RNA triplets. Such degeneracy in the code is compatible with the fact that $4 \times 4 \times 4$, or 64, different messenger or transfer RNA triplet combinations can be made of the 4 bases of the nucleic acid molecule, whereas only 20 amino acids must be specified by the various combinations. The evidence to this point suggests that every one of the 64 possible combinations may ultimately be found to be "meaningful" in the sense of specifying one or another of the 20 amino acid constituents of the end-product protein molecules.

It should be noted that this kind of degeneracy does not lead to ambiguity in the genetic code. To be sure, it means that messenger RNA molecules with different base sequences can govern the production of the same kind of protein. And the existence of such alternative "words" within the genetic language suggests that different species of organisms may employ somewhat different dialects in the nuclear books of instruction with which they control their cellular chemistry. Nevertheless, the code could still be universal in the sense that a given messenger RNA molecule, if capable at all of operating the genetic mechanisms of different types of foreign organisms, would always produce the same kind of protein molecules. Not only did Bonner's successful cross-breeding of the genetic mechanisms of pea plants and *E. coli* bacteria strongly suggest such universality in the genetic code, but the recent substitution of mammalian for *E. coli* cell-free extracts in experiments with synthetic messenger RNA has provided further confirming evidence. While much less work has been done with mammalian than with bacterial components, it has at least been established that the messenger RNA triplets that evoke specific amino acids in the finally fabricated protein molecules are the same for mammalian as for bacterial systems in the case of the half-dozen kinds of messenger nucleic acid that have been tested.

In general, while making allowance for some degree of variation from species to species in the details of the genetic mechanisms, biochemists today are confident that the genetic code has essentially been "broken"—that they are on the point of being able to line up every possible messenger RNA triplet with a particular amino acid in the resulting protein molecule.

But the specific sequence of amino acid segments in the manufactured protein molecules determines their catalytic properties and therefore controls the specific set of chemical reactions that take place in the cell. Therefore, the solution of the genetic code in this way implies the ultimate ability of the scientist to "read" the molecules of messenger RNA (or the nuclear DNA which produces them) and thereby learn the properties of the cell whose metabolism they control—whether the cell is to have the properties of pea plant or intestinal bacillus, for example. Inasmuch as the higher organisms, including man, are believed to employ the same system of genetic control (plus a few complications yet to be treated), the implications of this work are that one day the biochemists may even be able to determine the color of eyes or the shape of nose of a yet-to-be-developed human individual by analysis of the structure of the nucleic acid molecules in the cells of the embryo!

Before we move on to some of the additional complexities that characterize the structure and metabolism of higher organisms, we should make sure that we understand how the discussion of this chapter contributes to our basic thesis as to the purely physical origins of life.

The experimental evidence reported here can only strengthen our faith in the soundness of our nonvitalistic philosophy; for strong support for the thesis of the fundamentally physical nature of the life processes is provided by the success of the biochemists in extracting from living cells the pertinent nucleic acid/enzyme apparatus and in stimulating it to perform its architectural functions by means of the addition of nucleic acid from other organisms. And the successful employment of man-made chemicals for this purpose even verges on the dramatic in its demonstration of the workability of our physical explanations. Not even the evidence for the similarity of the principal features of the genetic mechanisms in all forms of life is particularly disturbing. To be sure, this might at first glance appear to be more reconcilable with the vitalistic view of the supernatural purposiveness of life than with the materialistic view that everything has happened as the result of the blindly probabilistic workings of evolution on the starting particles and immutable physical laws of the universe. However, there is really no great problem in imagining evolutionary developments that could have led to a considerable degree of ultimate standardization in the nucleic acid/enzyme mechanisms. And such evidences of variety as the degeneracy of the genetic code, with the accompanying implication of divergence from species to species in some of the details of the genetic mechanisms, seem comfortably consistent with our views of the normal consequences of the evolutionary processes.

As we address ourselves to some of the further complexities that characterize modern higher organisms we shall find that our considerations will continue to be intimately involved with the genetic mechanisms that have occupied so much of our attention to this point. We shall not be able to escape being enormously impressed by their overriding power and importance in the phenomena of life. While evolution is clearly the great technique employed by nature for developing its biological novelties, we shall find it easy to conclude that the genetic mechanisms may constitute the most ingenious and important invention yet achieved by the use of that technique.

BIBLIOGRAPHY

Asimov, I., *The Genetic Code* (The Orion Press, Inc., New York, 1962), chap. 6, "Locating the Code," and chap. 11, "Breaking the Code."

Beadle, G. W., "The New Genetics," in 1964 *Britannica Book of the Year* (Encyclopaedia Britannica, Inc., Chicago, 1964), pp. 45–72.

Bonner, J., R. C. Huang, and R. V. Gilden, "Chromosomally Directed Protein Synthesis," *Proceedings of the National Academy of Sciences,* vol. 50 (November, 1963), pp. 893–900.

Fraenkel-Conrat, H., *Design and Function at the Threshold of Life: The Viruses* (Academic Press Inc., New York, 1962).

Nirenberg, M. W., "The Genetic Code: II," *Scientific American,* March, 1963, pp. 80–94.

Stanley, W. M., and E. G. Valens, *Viruses and the Nature of Life* (E. P. Dutton & Co., Inc., New York, 1961).

part 4

From Amoeba to Man

chapter 14

The Living Cell

Throughout the preceding several chapters many references have been made to processes occurring in the cells of simple organisms. It has been assumed that the general background of the reader, supplemented by obvious extrapolations from our treatment of primitive coacervates, would make such references intelligible. However, before we can make much progress in rationalizing the evolutionary origins of advanced forms of life, we must devote some more specific attention to the properties of the cells of which all modern organisms are composed. Since this is not a textbook on biology, no attempt will be made to supplement what we have learned to this point so extensively as to end with anything like a complete treatment of the complex machinery of the living cell. Instead, our interest will continue to be narrowly confined to the general manner in which the operation of the physical laws underlying evolution has been able to create the advanced structure and metabolism of modern organisms.

In our early speculation about the primitive coacervates, before the nucleic acid mechanisms appeared upon the scene, we pictured the development of a number of cell-like characteristics. The external membrane, which made an individual out of a co-acervate droplet and makes an individual out of a modern cell, was such a characteristic. Another consisted of solid inclusions such as microsomes, on the surfaces of which certain kinds of chemical reactions might take place more rapidly. And we had no difficulty, in terms of the primitive mechanisms alone, in accounting for the existence of fluid-containing regions within the coacervates shielded by their own membranes from the chemical influence of the surrounding material. To the space-varying chemistry permitted by such complex structures we were even able to add time-varying chemistry by postulating suitable combinations of membrane selectivity and reaction time lags.

We have seen how the appearance of nucleic acid provided a powerful new line of evolutionary development. In recent chapters we have devised an imaginary course of natural history capable of refining the first fumbling architectural inclinations of nucleic acid into the remarkable precise and effective control properties of the modern nucleic acid/enzyme apparatus. In this way our discussion has bridged the gap between primitive co-acervates and modern cells with respect to the basic metabolic mechanisms underlying the control of growth and reproduction. However, we should not allow our recent preoccupation with the development of the genetic mechanisms to blind us to the fact that other refinements of the primitive mechanisms were also necessary if modern cells were to evolve from the coacervates. Let us consider two or three examples of these less spectacular, but nonetheless important, refinements that characterize living cells today.

First, consider the properties of membranes. When the subject was first introduced, in Chapter 7, it was pointed out that the physical laws that had to be obeyed by large-molecular-weight material in water would sometimes result in the formation of a semipermeable membrane enclosing the coacervate. In the ensuing treatment extensive use was made of the selectivity of such membranes—their confining effect on large molecules but relative permeability to small ones, for example. In general, the ability of an enclosing membrane to sustain substantially different chemical reactions in contiguous regions and to permit the interpenetration of selected products of these reactions is fundamental to the life processes. Therefore, it might be imagined that the economics of natural selection would have caused today's membranes to have much more highly developed properties than those of the primitive progenitors of cellular life.

And indeed this is true, although it is true in a somewhat curious way. Apparently, just as in the case of the nucleic acid/enzyme apparatus, the processes of natural selection have discovered one basic structure that is superior to all others; for electron microscope observations have revealed that all cell membranes have essentially the same two-dimensional arrangement of protein and lipid material. However, this does not mean that the permeability properties are the same for all cells. The important differences needed to meet the metabolic requirements of different cell species are produced by means of enzymes of a special class called *permeases*. Different varieties of permease can cause the standard membrane to pass or block the passage of different kinds of molecules. The combination of a suitable permease and the membrane also frequently results in one-way permeability, in which molecules of a certain kind will pass through the membrane in one direction but not in the other, even though they have to oppose a strong concentration gradient in their migration. It is easy to see how valuable this property can be in permitting a cell to extract selected ingredients from the surrounding fluids and concentrate them internally.

Another example of a detail of cell structure that must certainly have undergone extensive evolutionary refinement consists of the solid inclusions in the cytoplasm—the microsomes—that we have seen play such an important role in the nucleic acid control of protein formation. In 1956 the Romanian-born American biochemist George E. Palade, by a combination of electron microscope and chemical techniques, was able to show that the "working parts" of the microsomes consist of a myriad of very small subparticles, or *ribosomes,* that are densely distributed over the surface of the much larger microsomal particles. Each ribosome is of about the right size to support a single molecule of messenger RNA while it engages in its process of multiple marriage with the amino-acid-conveying transfer RNA molecules.

In addition, the ribosomes have been found to possess a special chemical composition that presumably contributes to their mission. They themselves contain RNA, mixed in about equal proportions with protein. Apparently this ribosomal RNA does not perform any control function of the kind that we have come to expect of nucleic acid. Instead, its binding with protein appears only to provide a surface with properties favorable to the attachment of the messenger RNA molecules that do participate in the control activities.

Incidentally, studies of the ribosomal processes have led to the conclusion that the life of the messenger RNA molecule is frequently a short one after it has stretched out on the ribosomal surface. In bacteria, at least, it lasts for only two or three minutes before it breaks up and its fragments float away.* Experiments employing radioactive tracer elements, by means of which determinations can be made of the time intervals involved in the capture of amino acid segments by transfer RNA and the subsequent assembly of the segments into protein molecules under the guidance of messenger RNA, have shown that in two or three minutes only a few protein molecules can be constructed. Thus

---

* However, some messenger RNA, especially in cells of higher organisms, persists for much longer periods.

the formation of enzymes under the guidance of the nucleic acid mechanisms can be a very active process, with messenger RNA continually being manufactured by the DNA molecules and the ribosomes continually receiving newly arriving messenger molecules and then recleansing their surfaces after a small amount of protein-construction activity. It is only because every cell contains hundreds of microsomal particles each covered with thousands of ribosomes that this seemingly inefficient process can produce adequate numbers of protein molecules to sustain life.

Modern cells contain a number of different types of inclusions in addition to ribosomes. Some possess such complexity of structure and function that they are called *organelles,* or "small organs." The *mitochondria* constitute an important kind of organelle. They are rod-shaped and about one three-thousandths of an inch long. There are perhaps 2,000 of them distributed throughout an average cell. Each tiny mitochondrion is a complete processing plant that takes in a standardized raw material —the sugar *glucose*—and puts out, in addition to by-products, an energy-rich chemical—*adenosine triphosphate (ATP).* More than a dozen separate chemical reactions are involved in this transformation, and each reaction is catalyzed by a different enzyme. The mitochondrion must store all these enzymes as well as the intermediate products in a structure that permits the continuous assembly-line manufacture of its end product ATP.

ATP, sometimes called a coenzyme, differs from the nucleotide adenylic acid only in its possession of three phosphate groups instead of one. It is by all odds the most important source of chemical energy in present-day organisms. No modern cell could survive without it. And the origin of this vital ingredient is the complex chain of reactions, many of the steps of which are identical for man and dandelion, that continuously take place in the mitochondria.

One of the most conspicuous structural features of modern organisms is the cell nucleus. In terms of our previous discussion, it is easy to regard the nuclear structure as a straightforward example of the kind of "drop within a drop" development that we postulated for the later stages of coacervate evolution. Nevertheless, it seems likely that the kind of nucleus we now know, with its clear-cut membrane separating certain internal structures and organelles from others of quite different kinds in the surrounding cytoplasmic fluid, is a relatively late development. For bacteria and a few other primitive organisms do not have well-developed nuclear membranes, although they frequently exhibit other inclusions and organelles of a considerable degree of sophistication.

In short, modern cells differ from primitive coacervates not just in their possession of the powerful genetic mechanisms but also in their incorporation of other features of a degree of sophistication and refinement unheard of in bygone days. There is no reason for this to be surprising, in view of the inevitable ubiquity of the evolutionary effects on which all biological progress is based. However, it seemed worthwhile to call explicit attention to these other developments before proceeding to a consideration of what must be some fairly late evolutionary developments related, once again, to the genetic mechanisms.

For our treatment of the modern cell, cursory though it is intended to be, would yet be unjustifiably incomplete if it failed to describe some of the techniques employed today to hold together and protect the all-important book of instructions contained in the DNA molecules for directing the chemical activities in the organism. Specifically, we must examine the properties of modern cells that minimize the effects of chance on the architectural activities of the nucleic acid control mechanisms.

The problem we must consider is not fundamentally different from one which we encountered in connection with the reproduction of the early coacervates. When one of our primitive bags of chemicals broke up, we saw that the ability of any one of the resulting smaller droplets to support a chain of chemical reactions similar to that which had been responsible for the growth of the parent depended on whether chance provided that smaller droplet with an adequately representative inventory of ingredients. If so, the new individual could survive and grow; if not, death ensued.

The development of the genetic mechanisms would have modified the problem of viable heredity, but would not have eliminated it. In particular, as DNA molecules assumed control of the chemistry of the cell by means of the powerful enzymes they generated, the survivability of an offspring of an adult individual would have become less dependent on the chance incorporation in the offspring of many of the ingredients normally found in the parent; the strong directing influence of the enzymes would have quickly made up for any initial imbalance in the proportions of most of the vital juices. However, nothing could have made up for the absence of an important enzyme resulting from the accidental failure of one of the generating DNA molecules to be captured by the offspring when the adult broke up into smaller pieces. As cellular chemistry became more and more complex, requiring increasing numbers of different enzymes to direct the many separate metabolic reactions on which life depended, the problem of ensuring that the individuals of each new generation received a complete complement of the corresponding types of DNA molecules must have become more and more critical. It seems unlikely that modern cells, with their survival requiring the successful completion of complex reaction sequences depending on thousands of different enzymes, could ever have developed if a way had not been found to pass DNA along from parent to offspring in an orderly manner. Fortunately, orderly procedures were possible and evolution succeeded in finding one. All the principles governing continuity of general characteristics within species and inheritance of detailed characteristics by individuals derive from the nature of the particular procedure that is now universally employed by living organisms for the precise handling of DNA.

The processes we are about to consider occur in the nucleus. With a small exception, to be discussed later, that is where all the DNA of the cell resides. In very primitive organisms such as bacteria, in which a definite nucleus/cytoplasm boundary is hard to detect, there is still a localized nuclear region within which the processes in question take place.

The key to the modern genetic protection mechanisms is packaging. Within the nucleus the thousands of different DNA molecules do not simply mill around, each performing its functions of self-replication and manufacture of complementary RNA molecules independently of the rest. Instead, the DNA molecules carry, a big step further, the long-chain structural concept that led to their own formation. They themselves hook together end to end, thereby forming nucleic acid "strands"—giant giant molecules composed of individual DNA components, each of which is already a giant molecule because of its own linking together of hundreds or thousands of nucleotides. In the cell of a complex organism there may be thousands of different DNA molecules strung together to form *each* such gigantic array. All of such strands or arrays possessing the same configuration of DNA molecules then line up side by side, along with some protein material about whose functions we shall later speculate. The resulting package is called a *chromosome.** The separate types of DNA molecules that compose the chromosome are called *genes*.

---

* Evidence suggests that, in most cells, there are only a few copies—perhaps only one—of each type of giant giant molecule. However, certain special cells, such as those in the salivary gland of the fruit fly, develop giant chromosomes containing thousands of times as much DNA as the average cell. In such special cases the chromosome appears to be a bundle of thousands of parallel and identical strands of DNA.

Higher organisms package many more different genes in each chromosome than do lower organisms, in order to carry the book of instructions that directs the complex chemistry of the cell. Frequently there are also more chromosomes. Thus only 8 chromosomes are found in the nuclei of fruit-fly cells, 46 in those of human cells.

Each strand of a chromosome acts partly as if it were a single molecular entity, partly like a loose aggregation of separate molecules. It reproduces itself as a unit—each ordered array of DNA molecules begets another similarly ordered array of the same types of DNA molecules. On the other hand, the individual DNA molecules seem able to perform their chores of manufacturing messenger RNA independently of one another. But in the movement of DNA from the nucleus of an old cell to that of a new one, during cell division, again unit action occurs: the separate DNA molecules are evidently tied together tightly enough that only complete strands participate in the migration.

It is, of course, cell division (*mitosis*) that plays for modern organisms the same kind of reproduction role that was once played by the physical forces of wind and wave as they broke into smaller pieces the primitive coacervates. Nowadays, however, it is the chemical state of the cell, rather than the physical conditions of the environment, that sets into motion the reproduction process. For example, it is possible that the complex interrelated chemical activities of mitosis are triggered by the approach to some built-in limit by the amount of DNA in the nucleus. Certain it is that, between successive divisions of a growing cell, the amount of nuclear DNA doubles.

Whatever may be the initiator of the processes of mitosis, the events that take place are known to every student of elementary biology. They are featured by a doubling of each of the chromosomes, a dissolution of the nuclear membrane, and an orderly migration of the two resulting sets of chromosomes to opposite sides of the cell. This is followed by a pinching together of the walls of the extended cell to form two separate cellular units and finally by the reestablishment of nucear membranes to contain the chromosomal material. The result is two cells instead of one, each possessing approximately half of the original cytoplasmic material and a set of nuclear DNA molecules identical with that with which the parent cell started life.

But we have explicitly localized these DNA packaging and distributing mechanisms in the nucleus. And references have been made to the fact that not quite all of the DNA of the cell is confined in the nucleus. The time has come to explain these references and to examine whether the existence and properties of the nonnuclear DNA can be accommodated in our picture of the DNA protection mechanisms.

The nonnuclear DNA—of an amount totaling a very few percent of that located in the nucleus—is found in some of the organelles of the cytoplasm. Mitochondria contain a small amount of DNA; so do *chloroplasts,* the chlorophyl-containing inclusions that perform photosynthesis in green plants. And this DNA clearly carries out genetic functions. This has been proved by experiments in which mutations were induced in the DNA of the cytoplasmic organelles by microbeams of ultraviolet radiation so directed as to miss the nucleus; physically abnormal organelles were then observed to occur in all subsequent descendants of the irradiated cell—showing that the undamaged nuclear DNA did not provide the structural specifications involved.

Further elaboration of the details of the nonnuclear genetic mechanisms, which is under way today in a number of research laboratories, is clearly of great scientific importance. The discoveries already made render it untenable to attribute *all* of the genetic control of an organism to the nucleus, as was once done. However, there is as yet no evidence calling for other major changes in the picture we have drawn of the genetic mechanisms.

For the experimental results are compatible with the hypothesis that the nucleic acid/enzyme processes related to the small amount of DNA of the organelles are just like those related to the much larger amount of DNA in the nucleus. The organelle DNA appears to manufacture messenger RNA which assembles corresponding enzymes. And, during mitosis, not only does the nucleus of the cell divide but so also do the organelles we are considering. It seems likely, too, that there are chromosomal mechanisms within the organelles that cause their genetic material to be accurately apportioned between parent and offspring, just as in the case of the nucleus. Thus, while it is interesting to speculate about the course of evolutionary development that has withheld from the nucleus of modern cells a few pages of the book of instructions that determines the chemical activities of the organism, there is as yet no indication that the anomaly of nonnuclear DNA requires any other major revision in our basic concepts pertaining to the genetic mechanisms.

Whether we have in mind the nuclear or the nonnuclear DNA packaging arrangements, it is clear that their net effect is to remove most of the element of chance from the basic mechanisms of genetics. The precise propagation of DNA molecules from one generation of cells to the next results in similar precision in the chemical and physical nature of the progeny. A splitting amoeba produces more amoebae, a paramecium more paramecia, a human cell more human cells. Even though the environmental conditions within which the new generations develop differ somewhat from those which nourished their parents—in temperature, chemical composition of the surrounding fluids, and so on —the relatively tight control over the specific cellular chemical processes exercised by the powerful protein enzymes, which in turn owe their creation to the specific roster of DNA molecules in the chromosomes, results in the remarkable continuity of species characteristics that features modern living forms.

A final comment about what may seem to be a curious inconsistency in one aspect of our argument would appear to be in order. We have just expressed admiration for the effectiveness of the chromosomal mechanisms in preventing change in the nature of the vital DNA material in going from one generation to another. And yet, only a chapter or so ago, our sympathies seemed quite different. For the development of our theories then we emphasized the existence of mechanisms capable of causing accidental changes in the ingredients responsible for the structure and metabolism of our organisms. We even went so far as to postulate the presence in the primordial seas of a small quantity of "nucleotide-linking catalyst" that encouraged the accidental formation of nucleic acid molecules of increased length and complexity. We could in addition have expressed satisfaction with the knowledge that thermal collisions and radioactive particles are also capable of causing mutations in the structure of nucleic acid molecules. Is our earlier emphasis on change consistent with our later emphasis on genetic stability?

Fortunately, it is not too difficult to reconcile these apparently incompatible points of view. During the era of preanimate coacervates, when extensive refinement in structure and metabolism was necessary before anything like living organisms could exist, there was obviously a premium on "mutagenic agents." This led not only to a corresponding emphasis in our literary treatment but probably also, by the normal economics of the evolutionary processes, to a relative abundance of such agents in the primordial seas. However, after eons of the trial-and-error refinement of the properties of organisms, a time must ultimately have come when random change in their properties was so much more likely to be harmful than helpful to the species that the advantage would all have been on the side of a combination of environment and organisms leading to relatively low rates of mutation in the hereditary mechanisms. Natural selection would then not only have brought to prominence such techniques for protection of the property-determining ingredients as we have just considered in connection with the nuclear DNA but might even have acted to diminish the abundance in the environment of some of the mutagenic agents. For example, if in certain regions primitive organisms were spilling into the seas such a quantity of nucleotide-linking catalyst as to lead to an undesirably high rate of mutation in the properties of most other organisms in the vicinity, there would have been a tendency for the main line of evolutionary development to be retarded in such regions; the result would ultimately have been the starving out of the undesirable mutagen-producing species as the course of evolution in remoter regions accelerated the proliferation of more modern strains.

Whether such developments occurred to slow down the rate of mutation or whether it was always slow (with the extensive accomplishments of evolution attributable only to the great time periods available), it is certain that today the combination of environment and organism seems usually to emphasize stability rather than change. When modern cells successively divide and send some of their precious DNA to guide the construction of new individuals, we expect the DNA that each new individual ultimately sends on to *its* progeny to be identical with that which it received, and we are rarely disappointed. It is likely that, on the average, each individual DNA molecule duplicates itself 100,000 or more times without the change of even a single atom in the thousands of which it is composed. Changes do occur occasionally, to be sure; if they did not, evolutionary development would be impossible. However, in terms of the few dozen or few thousand years over which the human species makes most of its observations, the protection provided to the large majority of the DNA by its nuclear environment and the precision of the mitotic distribution mechanisms, together with the relative scarcity of mutagenic agents, now contributes a remarkable degree of stability to the structure and metabolism of living organisms.

The sophisticated membrane properties of the modern cell, the ribosomal and mitochondrial structures, the nucleic acid/enzyme mechanisms, the chromosomal/mitosis processes—these and other features have been achieved at a tremendous cost of time and painstaking trial-and-error experiment. It is fortunate that the natural forces of evolution operate in such a way as to require convincing evidence of superiority before novel processes are allowed to replace such tried-and-true structural and metabolic principles.

BIBLIOGRAPHY

Asimov, I., *The Genetic Code* (The Orion Press, Inc., New York, 1962), chap. 10, "The Messenger from the Nucleus."

Asimov, I., *The Wellsprings of Life* (Abelard-Schuman, Limited, New York, 1960), chap. 13, "The Surface Influence."

Beermann, W., and U. Clever, "Chromosome Puffs," *Scientific American,* April, 1964, pp. 50–58.

Davidson, E. H., "Hormones and Genes," *Scientific American,* June, 1965, pp. 36–45.

Gibor, A., and S. Granick, "Plastids and Mitochondria: Inheritable Systems," *Science,* vol. 145 (Aug. 28, 1964), pp. 890–897.

Morowitz, H. J., *Life and the Physical Sciences* (Holt, Rinehart and Winston, Inc., New York, 1963), chap. 6, "Organelles," and chap. 9, "Cell Function."

Nirenberg, M. W., "The Genetic Code: II," *Scientific American,* March, 1963, pp. 80–94.

Oparin, A. I., *The Chemical Origin of Life* (Charles C Thomas, Springfield, Ill., 1964), chap. 4, "The Further Evolution of the Earliest Organisms."

Sager, R., "Genes Outside the Chromosomes," *Scientific American,* January, 1965, pp. 70–79.

chapter 15

Genetic Mechanisms and Cell Diversity in Multicellular Organisms

We must now attempt to bridge the gap between single-celled and multicellular organisms. Indeed, in this and the next chapter we must extend our considerations all the way up the scale of complexity to man himself. This may seem like a disproportionately small assignment of attention to the higher plants and animals. However, it has frequently been pointed out that practically all metabolic processes important to man are found in single-celled organisms and that, in terms of a really balanced appraisal of evolutionary accomplishments, man is much closer to amoeba than is amoeba to the nonliving materials from which it originated. Thus, in a book that seeks to trace the development of life from nonlife, the space assigned here to the amoeba-to-man period may in fact be disproportionately large.

But the close evolutionary kinship between the lower and the higher forms of life must not blind us to some important problems that arise in attempting to apply to plants and animals the lessons learned from a study of single-celled organisms. How, for example, do we reconcile what we have learned about the genetic mechanisms with the variety of cell types in a single plant or animal? Are the DNA molecules and the chromosomes different for heart cells, liver cells, and nerve cells? Or do all cells in the body carry the same genetic instructions? But if so, how can we account for the widely different chemical processes that must occur in the different kinds of body cells to give them such diversity in structure and metabolism?

For many years, evidence has been available to suggest that each cell in a complex organism must contain all the genetic information needed to specify the entire organism. As early as 1891 Hans Driesch obtained experimental results that seemed to require such a conclusion. He employed the common sea urchin in his experiment. Like all other animals, the sea urchin begins its development with a series of cell divisions. First the original fertilized egg divides into 2 cells; then each of the 2 cells divides, to make a total of 4 cells; then 8; then 16; and so on. Driesch discovered that if, in the 4-cell stage, the individual cells are separated from one another by violent shaking, each of the resulting separated cells will go on to develop into a complete sea urchin. Later experiments demonstrated the same principle with other animals, including vertebrates. In fact, the occurrence of identical human twins is ascribed to some form of intrauterine event that separates into two embryos the two cells that develop from the original fertilized egg.

Recent work by J. B. Gurdon, zoologist at Oxford University, has provided unusually convincing evidence for the thesis that the nucleus of every cell carries a complete book of instructions for the entire organism. Working with a species of African aquatic frog, he has shown that the original egg cell will develop into a complete and normal animal, even after its nucleus has been replaced by one removed from a specialized intestinal cell of a relatively mature embryo of the same animal.

Other experimental evidence is consistent with the implications of the work on embryos. Thus, the amount of DNA is found to be the same in liver cells, heart cells, skin cells, nerve cells, and so on.* Furthermore, the chromosomes, which can be seen with the optical microscope, have the same number and shape in all these cells. (The chromosomes are of different lengths, and they are not perfectly straight; their characteristic shapes make the matching of chromosomes from different types of cells more convincing than the mere obtaining of similar chromosomal counts would be.)

In higher animals, the single exception to chromosomal uniformity among different cell types is provided by the sex cells—the spermatozoa and ova of male and female. They have only half the number of chromosomes of all the other cells of the body—human sex cells possess only 23 chromosomes instead of 46, for example. But this fact has a compelling logic of its own. For the chromosomes in all the other cells of the body are arranged in pairs, and it has been established that one member of each pair owes its origin to the male parent, the other to the female parent. With the initial fertilization of the female ovum by the male sperm cell such a pairing of the chromosomes of the two parents is made, with the result that all further cells possess a genetic endowment contributed equally by father and mother. This provides a certain degree of redundancy for the DNA content of the nucleus: two genes instead of one are available to provide architectural control for the assembly of each enzyme required by the body, one in the chromosome supplied by the male parent and the other in that supplied by the female parent. These

---

* Insect cells containing giant chromosomes (Chap. 14) obviously constitute an exception to the general rule that all cells contain the same amount of DNA.

two DNA molecules may be identical, or they may be slightly different and therefore call for the construction of protein products of slightly different properties. If the two are different and one is markedly more effective than the other in enzyme production, we say that the gene from the corresponding parent is "dominant" and that the other is "recessive." Thus an individual with a gene from one parent calling for brown eyes and a gene from the other calling for blue eyes will always be brown-eyed, and so on. And by the later separation of the paired chromosomes and allocation of single members of each pair to newly formed sex cells the adult individual passes on to *its* progeny the genetic endowment of its own forbears. It is, of course, the statistics associated with the successive pairing of the chromosomes from different individuals from generation to generation that gives rise to the long-known and once mysterious facts of Mendelian genetics.

All this has a sort of simplicity and internal consistency that is convincing with respect to our confidence in the correctness of our understanding. There seems today little doubt that every cell except the sex cells in the body of a plant or animal contains exactly the same aggregation of DNA molecules, combined in exactly the same chromosomal packages, as every other cell.* Thus, if we ever succeed in *really* translating all aspects of the genetic code, we should be able to deduce all the genetically determined characteristics of an individual—color of the eyes, shape of the nose, contours of the face, pattern of the hairline—from analysis of the nucleic acid from a heart cell, a nerve cell, a skin cell, or a liver cell!

---

* There is, of course, the previously mentioned exception of the giant chromosomes. However, even in such chromosomes the sequence of specific DNA molecules in each strand of nucleic acid appears to be the same as in all other cells of the body; there are just more parallel strands of identical giant giant molecules.

But, returning now to our objective of reconciling the properties of single cells with the characteristics of higher organisms, we seem to have solved one problem only at the expense of rendering another one insoluble. For if, from the original fertilized egg on, every cell division results in the transmission to the new cell of exactly the same genetic specifications as those possessed by the generating cell, how can we account for the remarkable differences in the properties of the different types of cell that appear in a single plant or animal? After all, we have attributed to the genetic mechanisms overriding control of the chemical processes that make of any cell what it is. Therefore, if a heart cell and a liver cell have the same set of nuclear DNA molecules, how can they themselves be different?

What we are about to do is modify somewhat the picture we have drawn of the rigid control of cell chemistry by the DNA of the nucleus. We shall do this, not by denying anything we have learned as to the key architectural responsibilities of the nucleic acid/enzyme mechanisms, but by adding to our picture the structural modulating effects of other chemical agents. We shall learn that, in living organisms as in man-made buildings, it is sometimes the workmen on the job who *really* determine the details of the construction; the architect may be the designated designer, but the carpenters, plumbers, and electricians are also to be reckoned with.

For example, while the particular set of enzymes generated in the cytoplasm of the cell is determined by the genes in the nucleus, the effectiveness of the enzymes in performing their catalytic functions can be markedly influenced by chemical ingredients in the cytoplasmic fluid. Certain molecules can apparently wrap themselves around enzymes and inactivate them.* This

---

* The inverse also occurs. Sometimes attached molecules are able to increase the activity of enzymes.

phenomenon, in fact, frequently plays an important role in regulating cell chemistry, for evolution has worked in such a way that the end product of a chain of enzymatically catalyzed chemical reactions is often an inhibitor of one or more of the enzymes in the chain. This provides a kind of "negative feedback" around the reaction system, which slows or stops the generation of more end product if for any reason it begins to pile up in the cell. Useful though the sensitivity of enzyme effectiveness to other chemical agents may be in the normal metabolism of the cell, however, it also has the general result of making the cellular chemistry dependent to a degree on the cellular environment. If cells in different regions of a multicellular organism are washed by fluids of differing chemical content, the result can be different relative rates among the various enzymatically catalyzed reactions and, therefore, differences in the structure and chemistry of the cells.

And even more striking kinds of influence of the environment on the cellular chemistry have been demonstrated. In one of the pioneering experiments, the lowly intestinal bacteria—*Escherichia coli* bacilli—again came to the aid of biological science. The scientists in this case were French, F. Jacob and J. Monod, of the Pasteur Institute in Paris. In 1959 they arrived at the explanation of a curious form of adaptability of the *E. coli* bacilli. These organisms thrive in a culture based on the sugar *glucose*. If then transferred to a solution of the sugar *lactose,* the bacteria colonies become dormant. After a while, however, they resume their growth, and they thenceforth appear as able to employ lactose as food as they were previously able to employ glucose. The obvious question is: "What happened to the transplanted bacteria to overcome their initial inability to digest lactose?"

A part of the answer was obtained through the discovery that the new ability to employ lactose resulted from the eventual appearance in the cytoplasm of the bacilli of two new enzymes that do not appear when a glucose culture medium is used. One of these enzymes, it was found, modified the permeability of the outer cell membrane so as to permit molecules of lactose to enter the bacteria and thereby be exposed to the cytoplasmic chemistry. The other enzyme then acted on the lactose to break it down into the simpler molecular fragments that the *E. coli* metabolic mechanisms were equipped to use as food.

This, of course, answered one question, but it posed another. Why did the presence of lactose in the surrounding fluid happen to result in the appearance of just the kinds of enzymes required by the bacilli in order to profit by the new environmental conditions? By a series of very careful experiments, Jacob and Monod were able to answer this question also, or at least to push it back one step further into the fundamentals of the cellular mechanisms. For they showed that the lactose of the environmental fluid, on seeping through the cellular membrane,* acted as a sort of inhibitor to deactivate the product of one of the chromosomal genes. This gene, dubbed a "regulator" gene, through the usual nucleic acid/enzyme mechanisms, normally causes the production of a substance that suppresses the activity of two other genes in the nucleus—those capable of directing the manufacture of the two enzymes referred to. When the lactose "turned off" the inhibition normally caused by the regulator gene, the effect was to "turn on" the structural genes that permitted the cell to deal effectively with the new nutrient.

The work of Jacob and Monod has led to the discovery of many examples of the switching on or off of genes by chemicals supplied to the cells. The experiments have been extended to the tissues of rats and humans, and the generality of the phenomenon of "gene switching" has been confirmed. Indeed, it is now believed that hormones achieve their powerful effects primarily

---

* Some penetration occurs even before the new permeability-increasing enzyme is formed.

by such means. *Insulin* activates certain genes in the body cells to manufacture the messenger RNA that goes to the cytoplasm and assembles the kinds of enzymes that take care of fatty substances; *thyroxine* acts as a switch to turn on previously inactivated genes to make enzymes to control growth and metabolism; and so on.

Interesting visual evidence of the correctness of these theories has been obtained by means of microscopic observations. In the giant chromosomes of various species of flies a swelling or puffing has been observed at spots corresponding to the loci of particular genes, presumably when these genes are stimulated to activity by the chemical conditions in the cell. This puffing phenomenon seems to be related to the developmental stage of the tissue; for cells in different types of tissue, different gene loci show such signs of activity and at different developmental phases. Especially intense puffing of gene loci occurs at the time when the larvae start to pupate; this, of course, seems consistent with the very large changes in body chemistry that accompany metamorphosis.

One of the most intensive fields of biochemical research today consists of attempts to determine the detailed mechanisms involved in the phenomenon of gene switching. Clues have come from the laboratory of James Bonner at the California Institute of Technology. He and his coworkers have directed their attention to the protein material that, as we learned in the preceding chapter, is always associated with the DNA of the chromosomes. An important ingredient of this material is a protein called *histone,* or, when it appears in the nucleus as in this instance, *nucleohistone.* Working on the nuclei of cells from pea embryos, Bonner and his associates were able to show that 80 percent or more of the nuclear DNA is ordinarily bound to histone and that, furthermore, this histone-bound nucleic acid is inactive in the sense that it does not manufacture RNA. However, it was found possible to devise means for freeing the DNA molecules from histone, and they then became efficient RNA generators. Evidently, in natural cells, only one-fifth or fewer of the DNA molecules engage in constructive architectural activities at any one time. When a chemical ingredient invades a cell nucleus and switches on a previously inactive gene, apparently it does so by stripping away the histone that, by binding itself to the gene in question, has been keeping it inactive. This, of course, implies that there are many different varieties of histone molecules, each one specific to a particular DNA molecule, and that the hormones or other gene-switching chemicals are likewise specific in their histone-stripping properties. Whether these inferences are correct and, if so, just how these tailored chemical operations are brought about constitute important and unresolved problems of current biochemical research.

Whatever the detailed gene-switching mechanisms may be, it has been established that they are sometimes able to produce spectacular effects. For example, one investigator cultured cells from the nervous system of an amphibian until they developed properties identifying them as early pigment cells with a characteristic content of pigment granules and a star-shaped contour. He then removed the cells from the culture medium, washed them, and placed them in a different medium. As a result some of the cells, without undergoing division, appeared to change their properties entirely, even going so far as to develop muscle fibrils with a recognizable cross striation, as though the cells had changed their type from nerve to muscle cells.

There is also the curious adaptability of certain unicellular organisms such as various *Naegleria* species. They move around in an amoeboid form when they are on a relatively dry substratum in the presence of bacteria; but when they are surrounded by more or less pure water, they change their structure entirely and develop flagellae at one end, with the whole body elongated into a characteristic flagellate type. And a much more complex organism—the Mexican *axolotl*—which normally lives all its life and reproduces itself as a gilled newt in the water, can be turned into a land salamander at will by a single dose of thyroid. Despite the fact that the axolotl has lived out its life aquatically for thousands of generations, a fraction of a milligram of thyroxin, even from a sheep or fish, will bring out the latent salamander in a couple of weeks.

Indeed, the induction of major changes in an entire plant or animal by the influx into the cells of gene-switching chemicals is so common that it has been observed by all of us—in the metamorphosis of a tadpole into a frog or the pupation of an insect, for example. These changes can be induced at any time by dosing the young tadpole or larva with suitable hormones. Familiarity may blind us to the truly spectacular nature of such metamorphoses. The frog differs so much from the tadpole, and the butterfly from the larva, as to require that the nuclear DNA of each cell carry specifications for essentially two different species of organism, with switching arrangements to turn off one set of controlling genes and turn on the other upon receipt of the proper hormonal signal. In the face of such natural phenomena, one wonders whether the fairy-tale transformation of Cinderella's white mice into footmen was so far-fetched after all!

In summary, the modulating effects of externally supplied chemicals on the catalytic effectiveness of the enzymes and the even more powerful gene-switching capabilities of hormonal and other ingredients can cause different groups of cells in the same organism, despite a common genetic heritage, to develop widely different structural and metabolic properties. In principle, therefore, all that is necessary to account for cell diversity in complex organisms is a convincing explanation of how natural causes result in the imposition of different chemical environments on the different types of cells. The embryologists have been struggling with this problem for over a hundred years. In the next chapter we shall complete our case for the purely physical basis of the structure and metabolism of higher plants and animals by invoking some of the evidence from embryology for the physical origins of differences in the environments to which different groups of cells are exposed.

BIBLIOGRAPHY

Barry, J. M., *Molecular Biology: Genes and the Chemical Control of Living Cells* (Prentice-Hall, Inc., Englewood Cliffs, N.J., 1964), chap. 6, "How Genes Control the Formation of Other Cell Molecules."

Changeux, J. P., "The Control of Biochemical Reactions," *Scientific American,* April, 1965, pp. 36–45.

Encyclopaedia Britannica, 1962 ed., article on "Experimental Embryology."

Gurdon, J. B., "The Transplantation of Living Cell Nuclei," *Advances in Morphogenesis,* vol. 4 (1964), pp. 1–42.

Herskowitz, I. H., *Genetics* (Little, Brown and Company, Boston, 1962), chap. 21, "Natural and Induced Chromosomal Changes."

Huang, R. C., and J. Bonner, "Histone: A Suppressor of Chromosomal RNA Synthesis," *Proceedings of the National Academy of Sciences,* vol. 48 (July, 1962), pp. 1216–1222.

Oparin, A. I., *The Chemical Origin of Life* (Charles C Thomas, Springfield, Ill., 1964), chap. 4, "The Further Evolution of the Earliest Organisms."

Prosser, C. L., "Comparative Physiology in Relation to Evolutionary Theory," in *Evolution After Darwin,* vol. I, *The Evolution of Life,* ed. by Sol Tax (The University of Chicago Press, Chicago, 1960), pp. 569–594.

Umbarger, H. E., "End-product Inhibition of the Initial Enzyme in a Biosynthetic Sequence as a Mechanism of Feedback Control," in *Control Mechanisms in Cellular Processes,* ed. by D. M. Bonner (The Ronald Press Company, New York, 1961), pp. 67–86.

Vogel, H. J., "Control by Repression," in *Control Mechanisms in*

Cellular Processes, ed. by D. M. Bonner (The Ronald Press Company, New York, 1961), pp. 23–65.

Waddington, C. H., *New Patterns in Genetics and Development* (Columbia University Press, New York, 1962), chap. 4, "Morphogenesis in Single Cells."

Wells, H. G., J. S. Huxley, and G. P. Wells, *The Science of Life* (Doubleday & Company, Inc., Garden City, N.Y., 1938), book 4, chap. 4, "The A B C of Genetics," and book 4, chap. 5, "The Growth of the Individual."

Zalokar, M., "Ribonucleic Acid and the Control of Cellular Processes," in *Control Mechanisms in Cellular Processes,* ed. by D. M. Bonner (The Ronald Press Company, New York, 1961), pp. 87–140.

chapter 16

The Structure of Plants and Animals

Our discussion to this point has led us to essentially the following picture of how cell differentiation occurs in plants and animals. As the fertilized egg cell undertakes mitosis—dividing first into 2 cells, then into 4, then 8, and so on—slight differences in the chemical conditions in the several cells cause corresponding slight differences to occur in their internal reactions. These differences affect the chemical composition of the fluid emanating from the cells and therefore supplement the already existing sources of diversity to cause still later cells to be even more varied in their properties. As the organism grows by further cell division, the compounding of effects ultimately results in the appearance of cells of widely differing structure and metabolism.

Some of the mechanisms that respond to environmental differences to yield different types of cells were discussed in the preceding chapter. Let us now consider more carefully how the local environment is able to interact with the cellular regulative mech-

183

anisms to produce the remarkable variety displayed by the cells of a higher plant or animal.

Perhaps a good way to start our considerations would be to clear up what might appear to be an inconsistency between our present thesis and experimental evidence we have considered earlier. Specifically, we need to reconcile Driesch's discovery that any of the early cells of a sea urchin embryo can develop into an entire animal with our present notion that differences must appear in the structure and metabolism of the first few cells of a newborn organism.

A Swedish embryologist, Sven Hoerstadius, resolved the apparent discrepancy. In a series of beautifully planned and executed transplantation and isolation experiments he was able to show that the cytoplasm of the sea urchin egg is not uniform throughout in its composition, but contains varying proportions of two different chemical agents that have important influences on cellular metabolism. One of these agents was found to be concentrated at one "pole" of the fertilized egg, the other at the opposite pole. Hoerstadius established that it was only because the early cell divisions involved cleavages parallel to the polar axis that the first few cells all possessed the same proportions of the two agents and were therefore able to develop into entire animals. If, however, by artificial means the initial cleavage was forced to occur along such a plane that most of one stimulating agent went into one cell and most of the other into the second cell, an entirely different result was obtained: when these two cells were separated, each developed into only part of an animal, and the particular organs which developed in one "half-embryo" were different from those which developed in the other. Evidently one of the two chemical agents discovered by Hoerstadius acted as a switch to turn on the genes responsible for the construction of part of the animal, the other as a switch to turn on those responsible for the construction of the rest. And these two stimulating ingredients were already localized in different regions of the cytoplasm in the original fertilized egg.

A similar polarity of the original egg cell has been demonstrated for many other species. In some cases, at least, gravity appears to be the principal factor that causes the separation of the different ingredients of the cytoplasm in the egg cell as it develops in the mother's body. This is true of frogs' eggs, for example. Their polar axes are easily visible because of color differences. The bulky and nutritive yolk settles to the bottom of the egg; most of the cytoplasm rises to the top. The cells that grow from the top half of the egg ultimately develop into the head parts of the frog; those that grow from the bottom half develop into the tail parts. Thus the top-to-bottom polar axis of the egg controls a most important structural feature: it determines the body axis of the developing embryo.

While the environmental factor determining the important body axis orientation is gravity, quite a different factor determines the plane of symmetry. This plane is ordinarily determined, for frogs, by the point of entry of the male sperm cell into the egg during the act of fertilization. The "circle of longitude" of the sperm entry point becomes the head-to-tail belly line of the animal, while the meridian on the opposite side from the point of entry becomes the line of the backbone.

As the embryo develops, other gross physical effects play important roles in determining the configuration of the body parts. The pressure of water that collects in the developing tissue is believed to be instrumental in producing and shaping some of the cavities required for the proper conformation of the organs. The rolling up of certain groups of cells to form tubes—the neural tube which gives rise to the nervous system, for example—probably occurs because the electrical attractive forces among the molecules of substances produced by the growing cells cause them to try to make as close surface contact as possible with one another.

Many such physical factors must operate in conjunction with the specific chemical properties of the cells to cause different parts of the growing embryo to form different kinds of structures. And with each such characteristic structural development the chemical nature of the cells involved also changes, to become even more different than before from that of other groups of cells in the same organism, thereby facilitating even greater future differences in development.

There is considerable evidence to support the hypothesis that chemical individuality of the cells usually develops gradually rather than abruptly. If, in a very young embryo, cells are surgically transplanted to the head region from a part of the organism that would ordinarily develop into a tail, the transplanted cells take on the characteristics of the material that surrounds them and grow into component head parts. But if such transplantation is deferred for a time, a sort of fixation of properties occurs so that, after the operation, the transplanted cells grow into taillike parts, despite the fact that they must then protrude from the head of the full-grown embryo. The steady continuity in the development of the chemical fixation of the cells is shown by other observations: at intermediate stages of growth a small group of cells transplanted from any part of the tail region of the embryo will develop into an entire tail; later cells transplanted from a particular part of this region will develop into only a specific part of the tail. With the passage of time the cells seem to become more and more specialized and therefore more limited in the range of structure they are able to develop into.

An exception to the gradual nature of cell differentiation sometimes occurs when two previously separated parts of a growing embryo come together. The classical example of this phenomenon is the formation of the crystalline lens in the eye of a vertebrate. By following the gradual development of the embryo (of a chicken, for example), it was learned that the main body of the eye is formed from brain tissue by a sort of dimpling or hollowing-out process. This results in an "eye cup," whose open end gradually grows toward the layer of skin that surrounds the brain parts. When growth finally brings the rim of the eye cup in contact with the surrounding skin, some sort of reaction occurs that causes the circular sector of skin contacted by the cup to embark upon a new process of cellular development. Before long, this piece of skin thickens, detaches from the surrounding tissue, shapes itself into a lenticular structure, and becomes incorporated into the eye cup to form the crystalline lens upon which clear vision ultimately depends.

Research has confirmed the validity of the obvious inference: the tissue forming the eye cup in the brain structures contains a chemical which, upon contact with the surrounding skin, triggers metabolic processes that result in the formation of a lens. It has even been shown that the triggering substance is versatile enough to induce the formation of lens structures in other kinds of skin than that of the head region. The eye cup, for example, can be transplanted to the flank; upon contact with this kind of skin, a lens is formed. Or skin from another part of the body can be substituted for the head skin in the vicinity of the eye cup—upon contact of the two kinds of tissue, a lens develops. Evidently the stimulating ingredient in the eye cup is able to trigger the genes in the cells of any of the organism's skinlike tissue to reorganize their metabolic processes in the way necessary to develop a crystalline lens.

The stimulating ingredient is even more versatile: for example, the eye cup of a frog can induce a lens in head or flank epidermis of a salamander embryo.* However, the lens induced has the specific characteristics of a salamander eye, rather than a frog eye. Evidently the inducing substance from the eye cup is a chemical that is able to switch on the genes in the cell nuclei of various species to initiate the chemical processes resulting in a lens. However, the architectural details of construction are coded in the genes, and they are different for different species.

Again, when flank skin of a frog embryo is transplanted to the head of a young salamander embryo, the new chemical environment induces the transplanted skin to form head structures. But in doing so it follows its own genetic repertory and manufactures the horny jaws and teeth characteristic of the frog instead of the dentine teeth characteristic of the salamander. The explanation is, once more, entirely consistent with the picture we have developed of the genetic mechanisms. All cells in the frog contain genes capable of directing the formation of any of the many body structures, and the cytoplasmic chemicals of the flank skin cells still permit considerable flexibility in their ultimate development. When stimulated by the kind of chemical that switches on the genes appropriate for the generation of headlike structures, these flank skin cells proceed to form such structures. However, whether in the original frog body or transplanted to another species, the particular structures formed must be controlled in their detailed architecture by the genes of the frog. Hence the transplanted tissue must give rise only to froglike, not to salamanderlike, structures.

An embryological problem of unusual importance and difficulty is posed by the nervous system. How can we account for the enormous mass of specialized nerve cells (*neurons*)—10 bil-

---

* In embryos the immunological reactions that cause transplanted foreign tissue to be rejected do not occur. Hence transplantations are possible not only between different species but between different genera, families, orders, and classes. For instance, mouse tissue can grow in the chick embryo.

lion of them in a single human animal—that seem able to extend their tiny fibers many inches or even a few feet to make highly specific connection with other nerve cells or sense organs? To be sure, the general notions we have developed as to how cells in the embryo become more and more specialized can cause us to feel that the natural physical and chemical effects we have been dealing with might be adequate to produce even as strange a structure as that of the nerve cell. But how are we to explain the fantastically complex "wiring diagram" that appears to govern the interconnections of so many separate neuronal units?

Even before we have discovered the physical mechanisms underlying the construction of the nervous system, we can form some appreciation for the sheer bulk of information that would have to be handled in just specifying a definite pattern of neuronal interconnections. For most of the 10 billion neurons of the human nervous system connect, not just to one other nerve cell, but to many: the average is approximately 1,000 connections per neuron! And by no means all of these connections go to nearby cells; hookups to cells in entirely different parts of the nervous system are common. Thus, to describe in straightforward chart form the wiring diagram of the human nervous system, we would have to number the particular neurons from 1 to 10 billion and then write down for each a list of the approximately 1,000 other neurons to which it connects. We would end with a table of 10,000 billion numbers, with each number, on the average, containing 9 or 10 decimal digits!

But we have learned that the genes constitute the blueprint for the details of construction of the organism. Could they carry, in their four-letter nucleotide code, the equivalent of such a table that could in some way direct each neuron to make the right connections with its neighbors? The answer is no; they could not. We do not need to have a model of any particular physical process for enforcing neuronal wiring to be sure of that conclusion, for it rests solely and surely on the information-handling capacity of the genes. To be sure, the human genes do carry a great deal of information. There are several thousand genes in each of the 46 chromosomes, and each gene is a molecule of DNA containing a string of some thousands of nucleotides. The result is a "message-carrying capacity" equivalent to that of at least several dozen large printed volumes. While this is no small library for the nucleus of each of our billions of cells to be carrying around, it still falls far short of what would be required to "write down" the wiring diagram of the neurons in the way we have specified. And even if we could somehow squeeze this information into the genes, we would then have no room left over for all the other, nonneural, specifications that cause us to turn out to be humans rather than mosquitoes!

Obviously, the notion of the detailed genetic control of the interconnections of the neurons is untenable. What about the opposite assumption—that the neurons in the embryo just "grow like Topsy" in uncontrolled fashion, making random connections as they come in contact with one another? This assumption depends for its credibility on the theory that learning processes are subsequently able to strengthen and weaken the various neuronal connections so as ultimately to provide the coordination of physical and mental activity that constitutes the unique accomplishment of the nervous system.

In the higher animals, at least, any general theory of neuronal connectivity must be able to account for the phenomena associated with vision. In the human, more than half of the several million nerve fibers that leave the brain for other parts of the body go to the eyes. If a random-connection/subsequent-learning theory is the complete answer to our information-handling problem, we would expect that meaningful visual patterns would not occur in newborn animals, but would arise only after a period of trial-and-error learning. One of the most interesting experiments testing this hypothesis was performed by R. W. Sperry, Professor of Biology at the California Institute of Technology. In his work he took advantage of the fact that the nervous systems of many lower animals possess a regenerative capacity: if nerves are cut, they grow back and ultimately function once again. Sperry was therefore able to establish, in an adult toad, the equivalent of a "newborn" visual system. He performed an operation wherein the optic nerves were cut and reconnected inversely—that is, the right eye was connected to the nerve from the brain that previously had gone to the left eye, and vice versa. Of course, in such an operation, "reconnection" consisted only of butting the cut ends of the nerves together and waiting for natural processes to reestablish connections from the many tens of thousands of cut fibers to the brain. Even in an uncut optic nerve, these fibers cross and twist in what appears to be a highly random fashion. In view of such twistings and turnings (which are also characteristic of the human optic nerve), it had always seemed hard to believe that there was any precise built-in pattern of interconnection between retinal receptors and neurons in the brain; such anatomical observations had lent strength to the hypothesis that visual capability was acquired through learning, and not wired in.

Yet, after a few weeks, the toad was able to see again, apparently as well as ever! Certainly, the presence of a moving fly within its normal range of vision caused it to react in toadlike manner by darting out its tongue for the food. This and other tests led to the conclusion that, somehow, the fibers of the neurons of the visual cortex of the brain had managed to seek out and reconnect themselves, one by one, with the receptor cells of the eye in such a way as to reestablish in the brain a clear image, with normal topological properties of up/down and right/left continuity. That this had nothing to do with learning was proved by an interesting anomaly in the toad's new behavior: If a fly appeared opposite the toad's right eye, it darted its tongue out to the left to attempt to capture it; if the food appeared to the left, the toad would always strike to the right. To the animal, since the optic nerve of the right eye was connected to the part of the brain designed to be used with the left eye and vice versa, the image formed in the right eye always appeared to be coming from the left and the image formed in the left eye always appeared to be coming from the right. No amount of experience ever caused the toad to learn to correct its mistake. It was obvious that the left-ness and rightness of the vision were "wired-in" and not learned concepts.

Sperry's experiment was only one of many which have established that, despite the obvious ability of parts of the brain and nervous system to adapt and presumably modify themselves through learning, there is also a great deal of permanent wiring involved. Many of the neuronal interconnections are formed during the embryological development period, and they are formed precisely, in the sense that the right neurons are tied to one another or to just the right sensory receptors or motor effectors. Thus the hope that learning processes alone would provide a solution for our interconnectivity problem has proved to be a false one. The problem is still with us.

It is safe to say that no one yet knows for sure what physical or chemical factors are involved in the phenomenon of embryological neuronal wiring. However, there is a general hypothesis that seems able to account for most of the observed facts. This hypothesis is suggested by studies of the movements of cells in tissue cultures. Individual cells can be broken loose from the tissue of which they are a part and mixed with other cells in a liquid suspension. If in this way different types of cells—kidney and cartilage, say—are mixed together, a curious sorting out occurs. Under the microscope the cells, on encountering one another, are seen to slide over each other's surface in seemingly aimless fashion but with the ultimate result that cells of the one type seek out one another and aggregate in one lump or layer, while cells of the other type form their own similar but separate association. Experiments have been performed with solutions containing several different types of cell, with the same results. Evidently, chemical substances in the cells result in attractive or cohesive forces, specific to cell type, that tend to cause like cells to stick together, unlike cells to remain unconnected.

The extension of this principle to the formation of the connections between retinal receptors and cortical neurons in the visual system, for example, involves the following line of speculation. The receptor neurons in the retina of the eye are assumed to contain two separate chemical ingredients that vary in concentration in accordance with the position of the neuron on the retina. One of these chemical ingredients might appear in very small concentration in the rods and cones located at the extreme left-hand side of the retinal field, with the concentration of this ingredient increasing steadily across the retina to reach a maximum at the extreme right-hand side of the field. Similarly, the other chemical ingredient might show concentration increasing progressively from the bottom to the top of the retina. With such an arrangement, the relative proportions of these two chemical ingredients in a given receptor neuron would provide an accurate indication of the position of the neuron on the retina, both left and right and up and down. Similar concentration gradients are presumed to exist in the interneurons and the neurons in the brain with which the retinal receptors need to be ultimately connected. The embryonic growth process is assumed to be dynamic enough to cause each outgrowing nerve cell fiber to wander close to a wide range of candidate terminating cells. By the operation of attraction or cohesive forces similar to, but much more specific than, those required to explain the sorting out of dissimilar cells in liquid suspension, the searching nerve fiber is assumed able to seek out and make connection with receiving neurons of similar composition of the two key chemical ingredients. In this way there results a continuous one-to-one correspondence between points on the retina and those on the visual cortex of the brain, and the picture we finally see is coherent and unscrambled.

Future work may or may not confirm the controlling role of "connectivity" ingredients in determining the built-in wiring of the nervous system. If not, however, it seems inevitable that some other effect will be discovered that produces the same result—an ability of growing nerve fibers, through physical or chemical interaction with the local environment, to search out and connect to other specific neurons or terminal organs. The embryological prewiring in the nervous system will almost certainly turn out to employ mechanisms that differ only in degree, but not in quality, from those which control the development of structure in the rest of the organism.

Whether our concern is the development of neurons or of heart, liver, or skin, it now seems clear that the genes exercise architectural control over a growing multicellular organism by a combination of direct and indirect methods. Their delineation of the structure of the enzymes, which in turn specify the chemical reactions permitted in the growing cells, is an important direct method of influencing the final outcome. However, we have seen that the physical and chemical conditions of the extranuclear environment are also vitally important—that local physical forces distort and shape the growing tissue and that chemical agents in the surrounding fluids enter the cells to modulate the enzymatic reactions in the cytoplasm and to trigger on and off individual genes in the nucleus. To be sure, these local physical and chemical environmental factors are themselves results of the previous detailed development of the various parts of the organism which, in turn, depended on the genetic mechanisms and the local environment, and so on back to the initial fertilized egg. Thus it is still correct to say that the genetic mechanisms exercise primary architectural control over all the design features of the organism. However, they do not do so by means of a direct reading out of the nucleus of completely detailed specifications for each cell, followed by a single-minded manufacturing operation that follows such detailed instructions to generate the specified product, without regard for what may be happening in other nearby cells. Instead, the genetic mechanisms seem to have learned how to minimize their own detailed architectural chores by supplying to each cell a sort of do-it-yourself kit of structural and chemical features that automatically causes the cell to develop properly through the normal operation of physical principles as it interacts with the local environment that it and its neighbors continually create and modify. The result is the scene of activity constantly viewed by the embryologist—a delicately balanced and fantastically complex interplay between the genetic mechanisms of the cells and their varied and changing surroundings. This is the secret of the diversity of structure and metabolism that makes multicellular plants and animals possible. Only by such methods is nature able to mold its raw materials into such an impressive end product as a living higher organism—a sea urchin, or a man.

A final comment about the evolutionary origin of the mechanisms on which multicellular life is based may be in order. For despite the compelling nature of the evidence, normal human experience does not seem compatible with the conclusion that such remarkably complex and intricately interrelated mechanisms could have arisen solely through the blindly probabilistic workings of evolution. The antidote to such a feeling of skepticism is a reconsideration of the frequency of past occurrence of the typical sequence of small accidental change of structure or metabolism, competition for survival, and ultimate proliferation of the best-adapted species. The fantastically large number of such small refinements that must have taken place among trillions of

individual organisms during billions of years is also far beyond
normal human experience. The essence of the theory of evolution
is the balancing of the near inconceivability of its accomplishments against the correspondingly near inconceivability of its
painstaking attention to detail.

BIBLIOGRAPHY

Encyclopaedia Britannica, 14th ed., article on "Experimental Em-
bryology."
Encyclopaedia Britannica, 1962 ed., article on "Experimental Em-
bryology."
Waddington, C. H., *New Patterns in Genetics and Development*
(Columbia University Press, New York, 1962).
Wooldridge, D. E., *The Machinery of the Brain* (McGraw-Hill Book
Company, New York, 1963), chap. 2, "The Schematic Diagram of
the Nervous System."

Conclusion

Conclusion

In the beginning there were the laws and the particles. The laws caused the particles to aggregate to form atoms of a limited number of types and properties and the atoms to fit together in specific molecular configurations.

In the atmosphere of the primordial earth the basic sources of energy—radioactivity, ultraviolet radiation, electric discharge, and heat—broke up some of the gaseous molecules into fragments that, on recombining, formed a number of heavy and relatively complex compounds, which drifted down into the sea. The new ingredients included energy-rich molecules which, by temporarily hooking on to other molecular fragments, facilitated their participation in the formation of even more complex compounds. There were also amino acids, which sometimes linked together to form simple proteinlike substances; there were sugars, phosphates, and bases, which, under suitable conditions of temperature and juxtaposition, were occasionally able to form primitive precursors of the nucleic acids.

In isolated pools cut off from the major seas by seismic events, evaporation of most of the water greatly increased the rate of chemical activity. Within these pools the statistics of random combination of molecular fragments occasionally resulted in the creation of complex molecular assemblies, which constituted effective catalysts for specific chains of reactions among the available ingredients. Once in a long while the phenomenon of auto-catalysis occurred, resulting in closed cycles of self-amplifying chemical activity. Through the operation of the laws of physics that determine the properties of high-molecular-weight material dissolved in water, the new compounds had a tendency to collect in droplets, or coacervates. These bags of chemicals ultimately came to display lifelike properties, including the ability to "grow" and, under suitable circumstances, to "reproduce" their own kind.

Meanwhile, another important line of chemical evolution was developing. The simple nucleic acid molecules which continually and automatically formed in the "hot dilute soup" of the primordial seas began to exhibit interesting reproductive processes of their own. This first occurred in sophisticated types of coacervates which possessed certain kinds of catalytic ingredients as well as temporally varying cycles of chemical activity. Ultimately the random but thorough processes of evolutionary trial and error succeeded in combining a fortunate set of properties in the same coacervate. These properties included the conditions required for the precise self-reproduction of the "genetic" nucleic acid molecules as well as those needed to permit long "messenger molecules" of nucleic acid to stretch out on solid inclusions and form attachments with shorter "transfer molecules" of the same substance. The natural attraction of the unattached ends of the transfer molecules for other molecular species then yielded a spectacularly important by-product of these reactions—the manufacture of other complex organic compounds in addition to nucleic acid.

With the passage of time evolutionary refinement specialized the messenger and transfer molecules until the nucleic acid mechanisms became unusually effective in the assembly of protein enzymes. These powerful catalysts, in turn, ultimately took over control of the pattern of interrelated reactions that, finally, contributed to the "bags of chemicals" enough stability and metabolic sophistication to entitle them to be called "living organisms."

Along with the increased architectural effectiveness of the nucleic acid/enzyme mechanisms came other evolutionary improvements in the structure and metabolism of single-celled organisms. Membrane properties improved. Ribosomes and "organelles," such as mitochondria, appeared to contribute to the viability of the cell. The development of the nucleus facilitated complex chemical reactions by providing a degree of isolation between major metabolic subsystems. Additional ruggedness was provided by dividing the functions of nucleic acid between two different kinds of molecules and protecting, by means of the chromosomal mechanisms, those carrying the basic "book of instructions" for control of the structure and metabolism of the cell. These unusual packaging provisions resulted in such a precise means of nucleic acid distribution, during cell division, as to ensure the high degree of genetic stability appropriate to the relatively advanced evolutionary stage of modern life.

The economics of evolution even permitted capitalization on what might have seemed an important weakness in the cellular mechanisms: the sensitivity of some of the nuclear and cytoplasmic reactions to the influence of chemical agents in the environment. For the resulting nuclear gene switching and cytoplasmic modulation of enzymatic effectiveness made possible multicellular organisms by permitting different groups of cells to develop in different ways despite a common genetic endowment. And, because of the contribution of local environmental effects to the differentiation of the parts of the organism, the information content of the book of instructions in the genes could be enormously less than that required to code the detailed structure and metabolism of every cell into the nucleic acid molecules. Thus, complex organisms became practicable. Higher plants and animals, including man, were able to develop.

It can certainly not be claimed that the sequence of events just summarized has been documented, in this book or elsewhere, with anything like completeness. The time scale is so vast and the absence of corroborating paleontological evidence for some of the important steps is so complete as to render it unlikely that the speculative aspects can ever be entirely removed from this kind of narrative. It still appears necessary to invoke an element of faith if any story of the creation is to carry conviction.

To those who are inclined to believe in a lawful and orderly world, however, the present state of knowledge and theory offers considerable encouragement. Any self-consistent explanation of the origin of life in terms of purely physical, nonvitalistic principles, despite inaccuracy of detail, is a significant accomplishment. And such a spectacular biochemical success as the stimulation of cell-free extracts from bacteria into the manufacture of protein, by means of man-made nucleic acid molecules, comes close to the long-awaited demonstration that "life" can be synthesized in the test tube. Such developments must greatly enhance confidence in the thesis that proclaims the unity of biological and physical science.

Thus our narrative has carried us a long way toward the philosophic objective of establishing that physical principles alone are capable of accounting for all human observation and experience. Yet the story told here is obviously not complete; for the adequacy of physical science to account for the structure and chemistry of living organisms does not necessarily imply equal adequacy for the explanation of such seemingly nonphysical attributes as behavior, intelligence, and consciousness. As mentioned in the introduction, I have dealt with these matters in an earlier volume.* To me, at least, the evidence there considered seemed convincing for the conclusion that all aspects of behavior, including those which we call "intelligent," will ultimately be found reducible to the operation of a combination of physical principles not fundamentally different from that which underlies the design of advanced versions of man-made computing and logic machines. If that is true, there remain only the phenomena of conscious awareness to be accounted for in order to establish that all experience can be explained by the operation of a single set of natural laws. But there is a growing body of evidence attesting to an orderly and predictable interrelationship connecting the qualities of conscious experience with the physical condition of parts of the brain. We know, for example, that a signal sent from the brainstem to the cortex turns on or off the state of consciousness and that sensations of pleasure, pain, rage, horror, or ecstasy appear automatically in response to the injection of electric current into specific parts of the brain. In the earlier volume I interpreted such discoveries as indicating that conscious phenomena are suitable for inclusion in the subject matter dealt with by the laws and methods of the physical sciences.

To be sure, a mere formal transfer of the phenomena of consciousness out of metaphysics and into the realm described by the physical laws of nature would not "explain" the mystery of subjective awareness. However, as I observed in the introduction, physical science does not really explain any of its mysteries. Gravitational attraction and electric charge are essentially as inexplicable as consciousness; they seem better understood only because we have long since established that their effects are regular

* Dean E. Wooldridge, *The Machinery of the Brain* (McGraw-Hill Book Company, New York, 1963).

and predictable, not because we know what they "really" are. The available evidence is consistent with the expectation that the properties of conscious experience may ultimately be found to be as regular and predictable as are those of gravity and electricity. If so, it is inevitable that we shall eventually add the relationships between physical states of neuronal matter and qualities of subjective awareness to the laws which, along with the basic particles, make up the content of modern physics. And, for all its philosophic importance, this will then be but an incident in the continuing development of our understanding of the body of natural law that determines the course of observable events.

The same body of natural law will then suffice to "explain" the formation of a distant nebula, the operation of a television receiver, the growth of a child, and the genius of an Einstein. Like other sweeping philosophic generalizations, this belief in the unity and adequacy of science cannot be proved to be correct—it is essentially an article of faith. However, it has a great advantage over other philosophies: this philosophy, uniquely, derives further strength from every new scientific discovery. This is because, in science as it is actually practiced, all theory is nonvitalistic: the postulate of a single set of natural laws is the starting point for all modern scientific explanation. And spectacular advances in our understanding of the universe are continually being made by application of this simplifying assumption.

Thus, in the last half of the twentieth century, the case for the unity and adequacy of science has become a strong one. Future discoveries may soon render inescapable the conclusion toward which science has for so long been trending—that the regular and predictable operation of a single body of physical law is sufficient, without supplementation by any form of extra-scientific or "vitalistic" principle, to account for all aspects of human experience.

Index